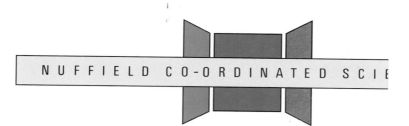

NUFFIELD CO-ORDINATED SCIE

EARTH AND SPACE

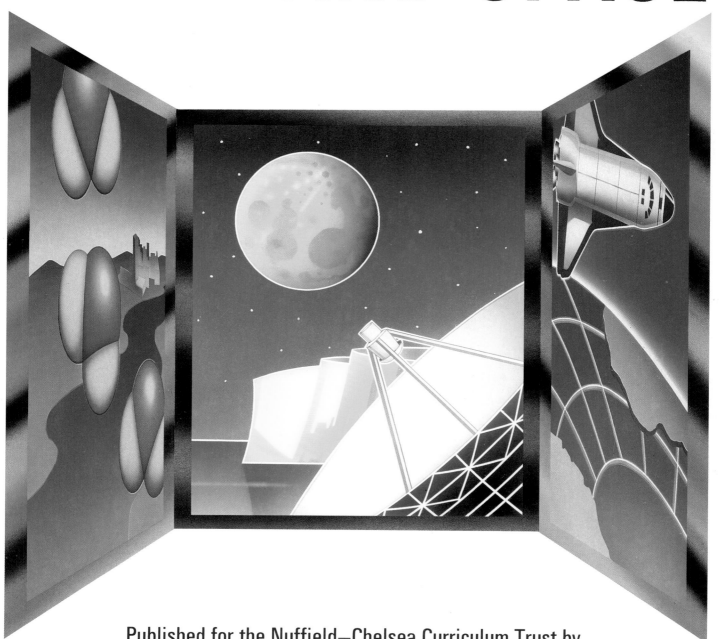

Published for the Nuffield—Chelsea Curriculum Trust by
Longman Group UK Limited

General Editors, Nuffield Co-ordinated Sciences
Geoffrey Dorling
Mark Ellse
Andrew Hunt
Grace Monger

Author and General Editor, Earth and Space
Mark Ellse

Contributors
David Adams
Eileen Barrett
Brian Cant
Alan Cochran
Keith Moseley

Longman Group UK Limited
Longman House, Burnt Mill, Harlow, Essex, CM20 2JE, England and
Associated Companies throughout the World.

First published 1992
Copyright © The Nuffield–Chelsea Curriculum Trust 1992

Illustrations by
Hardlines, Mark Peppé and Lyn Williams
Cover illustration by Plus Two Design

Filmset in Monotype Lasercomp Times Roman

Printed in Great Britain by Butler & Tanner Ltd., Frome and London

ISBN 0582 09397 X

The Publishers' policy is to use paper manufactured from sustainable
forests.

Contents

Acknowledgements

Anglesey Mining PLC: 2.3 fig 1

Catherine Blackie: page 26 (Coniston slate)

Bruce Coleman Ltd: Nigel Blake page 1; Mark Boulton 1.1 fig 3; Jane Burton 2.6 fig 6; Jeff Foott 1.2 fig 4; Steven Kaufman 3.2 fig 2; John Murray 2.5 fig 6; Charlie Ott 2.4 fig 3

Documentation Française: 3.2 fig 4

Geoscience Features: page 26 (sandstone), 2.6 figs 2, 3 and 5

Robert Harding Picture Library: 2.1 fig 5; Thomas Laird 1.1 fig 1

Landform slides: 2.1 fig 1, 2.4 fig 2, 2.6 fig 1

Frank Lane Picture Agency: page 26 (limestone pavement); G. P. Eaton 2.4 fig 1; US.DA Forest Services 2.5 figs 1 and 2

P. Morris: 2.1 fig 7

Keith Moseley: 1.1 fig 4, 1.2 figs 1, 2 and 3, 3.1 fig 2

The Natural History Museum, London: page 26 (feldspar granite); Martin Poulsford 2.5 fig 4

NHPA: 3.2 fig 1

North Yorkshire Moors National Park: page 13

R. K. Pilsbury: 1.2 fig 6, 1.4 figs 5a to 5e, 1.4 figs 6a to 6c

Rex Features: 2.3 fig 3, 2.5 fig 5

Rida: David Bayliss 2.1 fig 2, 2.4 fig 4, 3.5 fig 3; Richard Moody page 26 (pillow lavas)

Science Photo Library: Alex Bartel 3.7 fig 2; Julian Baum 3.7 fig 4; Simon Fraser 2.1 fig 4, 2.4 fig 5; Astrid and Hans-Frieder Michler 3.4 fig 1; David A. Hardy 3.2 figs 5a and 5b, 3.5 fig 4; Vern Hodgson 3.2 fig 6; Nick Jackson 3.6 fig 1; MAPTEC International Ltd 3.7 fig 3; Michael Marten page 26 (Lewisian gneiss); Peter Menzel 2.3 fig 2; Angela Murphy 1.2 fig 5; NASA page 35, 3.3 figs 3, 4, 5, 6 and 7, 3.4 figs 3, 4 and 5, 3.6 fig 5; NCAR 3.6 fig 6; NOAO 3.6 figs 4a, 4b and 7, 3.7 fig 9; David Parker 2.3 fig 4; Philippe Plailly 3.5 fig 5; Mikki Rain 3.1 fig 3; John Reader 3.5 fig 2; Roger Ressmeyer 3.3 fig 1, 3.7 fig 8; Peter Ryan 2.2 fig 4; John R. Sanford 3.4 fig 2; Sinclair Stammers 2.1 fig 3; James Stevenson 3.3 fig 2; U.S. Naval Observatory 3.6 fig 3

Telegraph Colour Library: J. Alexandre 3.5 fig 6

Zefa Picture Library: 1.1 fig 5, 3.7 fig 1

Topic **E1**   **Weather**

Section **E**1.1   **Air, hot and cold**

What's the weather like on the top of a mountain? Even if you have never been skiing, you know that it is usually colder when you are higher up. On average, the temperature gets over half a degree Celsius colder for every 100 m higher you climb. Weather scientists call this the **lapse rate**. This helps explain why so often there is snow and ice at the top of mountains, even in summer.

Figure 1
Snow on top of the Himalayas.

1 The top of Mount Snowdon is 1085 m high. How much colder is it likely to be there than at sea level?

2 What happens to the atmospheric pressure as you climb up a mountain?

If you want to understand why it is colder at the top of a mountain, think first what happens to a ball when you throw it up into the air. It slows down as it gets higher. It loses **kinetic energy** and gains **potential energy**. The same thing happens to the molecules in the air even though they are moving randomly. As they get higher, they travel more slowly. If the molecules are travelling more slowly, the temperature is less.

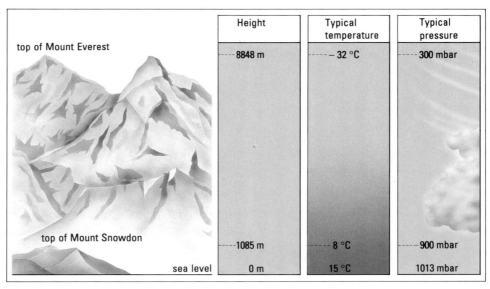

Figure 2
How temperature and pressure change with height.

	Height	Typical temperature	Typical pressure
top of Mount Everest	8848 m	−32 °C	300 mbar
top of Mount Snowdon	1085 m	8 °C	900 mbar
sea level	0 m	15 °C	1013 mbar

The air pressure, too, gets less as you get higher up. That is easy to understand. At sea level the whole depth of the atmosphere is pushing down. The thickness of air above the top of a mountain is much less, so the pressure is less.

Figure 2 shows a mountain with some temperatures and pressures marked. This is the normal state of the atmosphere. The temperature and pressure are greatest near the ground and decrease as you get higher.

Figure 3
The air inside the balloon is less dense than the air outside.

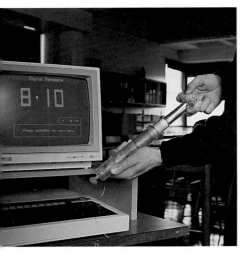

Figure 4
When the gas inside the syringe expands, its temperature drops.

Hot air rises

Figure 3 shows a hot-air balloon. The balloon rises because the air inside is hotter than that outside. Do you remember why this causes the air to rise? When air is heated, it expands and becomes less dense than the cold air around it. The denser, surrounding air pushes the hot air up. Any air, even if it is not part of a hot-air balloon, will rise like this if it gets hot. When the Sun shines, some parts of the ground get hotter than others. Air near those parts gets hotter and rises like an invisible balloon. Sometimes you can see the convection currents this produces, when movement of the air causes a **heat haze**. Sometimes you can see gliders or birds soaring on convection currents of air. Such masses of rising air are called **thermals**.

Have you ever wondered what happens to the hot air as it rises? Does this warm up the air at the top of the atmosphere? You know that the atmospheric pressure gets less as you get higher. What happens to gas as it rises and the pressure on it gets less? To understand, it helps to do an experiment in the laboratory.

Figure 4 shows a gas syringe connected to a sensitive thermometer. You can reduce the pressure by pulling on the plunger. That is rather like taking your sample of gas up a mountain. When you pull on the plunger, the pressure drops and the gas expands. But that is not the only thing that happens. When the gas expands, the temperature of the gas also drops. This helps us to understand what happens to hot air when it rises.

Air keeps rising as long as it is less dense than the surrounding air. As it rises, the pressure on it gets less, so the air expands. As it expands, it gets colder. The air stops rising when it has cooled to the same temperature as the air around it. Sometimes warmed rising air may ascend many kilometres before it cools to the temperature of the surrounding air.

Cold air sinks, because it is denser than the air surrounding it. This often happens at night in clear weather. Air above the hills cools quickly and drains into the valley bottom, pushing the warmer and less dense valley air upwards. This causes the unusual situation of cold air near the ground and warmer air above it. Weather scientists call this a **temperature inversion**. Cold air in hollows at night may make 'frost pockets' which can damage crops. The same process can bring hazards for drivers as it causes fog or ice on low-lying roads and motorways.

Figure 5
Fog often forms in cold air in valleys.

3 Think about the gas in the syringe in figure 4. What happens to the mass of the gas when you pull the plunger out? What happens to the density of the gas?

4 Have you ever noticed what happens to a bicycle pump when you are pumping a tyre up? The pump gets hot. Use what you have learned in this section to explain why this happens.

5 Energy is needed to make the gas in the bicycle pump in question **4** hotter. Where does the energy come from? Where does the energy eventually go to?

Section **E1.2**   **Water in the air**

Breathe on a mirror or another cold, shiny surface. What do you notice? The mirror becomes cloudy. Water vapour from the air in your breath condenses on the surface of the mirror. You may have noticed condensation on windows early in the morning. This water comes from the air in the room. The air around you is made up mostly of oxygen and nitrogen, with small amounts of other gases, but there is water vapour in it as well.

1 Where does the water vapour in the air come from? Give four sources.

Water gets into the air by evaporation from many different sources. Every time you put washing out on the line to dry, the water in the washing evaporates and ends up in the air. Evaporation takes place at all temperatures, but it is faster when the temperature is higher. As the washing dries, the air around the washing gets more water in it. If the air around the washing is very still, eventually it becomes **saturated** (full up) with water. Then no more water will evaporate.

When scientists want to talk about the amount of water in the air, they talk about the **humidity**. If the humidity is low, the air can take a lot more water. If the humidity is high, it can't. You may have used a **hygrometer** to measure relative humidity.

Hot air can hold more water than cold air, so if saturated air is heated, it can hold yet more water. But if saturated air is cooled, it can no longer hold all the water it contains. Some of the water condenses.

2 Why will washing dry faster on a warmer day? Why will it dry faster if the weather is windy?

Making clouds

Clouds form when water in the atmosphere condenses. Sometimes this makes small droplets of water and it is easy to see through the cloud. Sometimes the droplets are larger. Rain occurs when the droplets get too big to be kept up by the moving air particles. If a cloud forms near the ground, we call it mist or fog.

You can make a cloud with water vapour in a laboratory bell jar, but the clouds are more visible with methanol. A cloth wet with the liquid saturates

Figure 1
Where does this water go when the puddle dries up?

Figure 2
A hygrometer is used to measure how much water there is in the air.

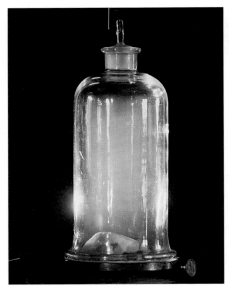

Figure 3
When the air in the bell jar expands,
vapour in the air condenses and forms a
cloud.

Figure 5
Cumulus cloud over Hawaii.

Figure 6
Cirrus clouds.

Figure 4
If a cloud forms near the ground, we call it mist or fog.

the air in the bell jar with vapour. When the vacuum pump is turned on, the air in the bell jar expands as some of it goes into the vacuum pump.

3 What happens to a gas when it expands? (Remember what you learned from the last section.)

The air in the bell jar gets colder when it expands, so it can no longer hold all the vapour that it did do. The vapour that comes out of the air condenses to drops of liquid and makes a cloud.

You know that air near the ground gets hotter as the Sun heats the ground during the day. At the same time, the air gains water vapour by evaporation from ground and sea, and from plant transpiration. So air near the ground gets moister as well as hotter before it rises. As this air rises, it gets colder and cannot hold as much water. The air first becomes saturated, and then water droplets start to form by condensation as it gets even colder. These water droplets make clouds like the one in the bell jar.

Air which contains water vapour can rise further than dry air. As the water condenses, it gives out latent heat. This energy keeps the air warmer and helps convection. Tall cumulus clouds formed in this way produce very heavy rainstorms, especially in intensely-heated tropical areas.

4 Use your library or a reference book to find out about clouds. Draw pictures of the different types.

5 Observe the clouds from your home and make a record of your observations. Which way do the clouds mostly move? Which clouds bring rain? What sort of clouds do you get in good weather?

6 After a few days of sunny weather, we often get thunderstorms. What is thunder? Why should good weather produce thunder?

Section **E**1.3   **Prevailing winds**

Convection works on a global scale as well as locally, though the circulation of the atmosphere is very complex and scientists still do not understand it. Areas where air is rising are called Low Pressure areas, or **lows**. These tend to produce clouds and precipitation. Where large masses of cooled air sink back towards the surface, there are High Pressure areas, or **highs**, with little cloud and more stable weather as the air gets warmer by being compressed and nearing the warm ground.

The Earth is roughly a sphere, and the Sun's radiation falls much more directly on the surface near the Equator than at the Poles. So you might predict that the air in contact with the Earth's surface near the Equator would be warmed and would rise. Cooler air from the Poles would flow in to take its place and a circulation would be set up like the one in figure 1. This simple idea of convection is called a Hadley Cell after George Hadley, who suggested it in 1735. In fact atmospheric convection is more like the more complex figure 2, suggested in 1951 by Erik Palmén.

1 Draw a diagram to show why land near the Equator gets hotter than land near the Poles.

Figure 1
A simple model of convection in the atmosphere.

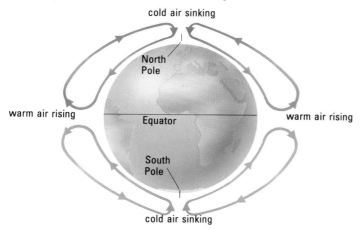

Figure 2
Palmén's model of convection.

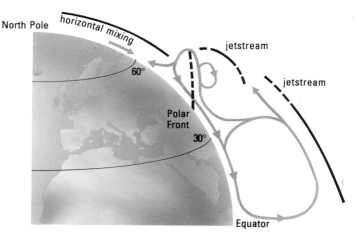

The effect of the Earth's spin

2 Find out the circumference of the Earth. Use this to calculate the speed of a point on the Equator.

The Earth spins (rotates) from west to east, making one complete turn per day. This means that the speed of a point on the Equator is one circumference per day (about 1700 km/h). But the speed at the Poles is zero. This difference in speed has an effect on the air masses as they move towards or away from the Equator. Friction between the Earth and the different layers of air speeds up air masses as they move towards the Equator and slows them down as they move towards the Poles. The result of all this is an actual global circulation like figure 3.

3 The **doldrums** is a name for calm areas along the Equator. Why is there no clear direction to the winds there?

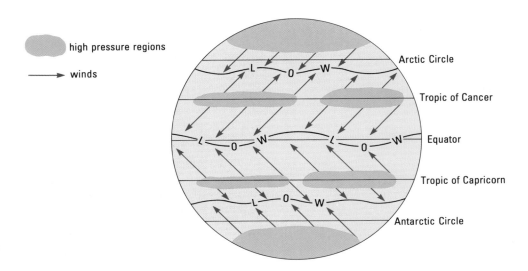

Figure 3
Convection and the rotation of the Earth produce these **prevailing winds**.

There are also large, fast-moving belts of winds in the upper atmosphere. These **planetary waves** follow a wavelike course and have **jet streams** at their core. They are important to air-route planners, but little understood as to their effect on weather systems.

4 Why should aircraft take account of the jet streams?

You know that the Earth's axis is tilted. This means that over the year, the part of the Earth that the Sun heats most strongly shifts between 23° north in June and 23° south in December. This shifts atmospheric circulation too.

Water has a much higher specific heat capacity than land, so lands warm up more quickly than oceans in summer, and cool down more quickly in winter. This tends to build up Low Pressure areas over the continents in summer, and High Pressure in winter. Land and sea areas are unevenly distributed, and this makes global circulation very irregular. On a local scale the same effect causes Land and Sea breezes that make British beach holidays chilly.

5 Why is there so often a wind from the sea onto the beach?

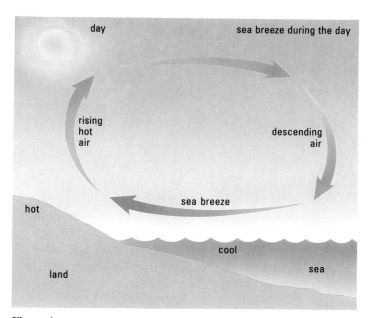

Figure 4
During the day, the land is hotter than the sea. This produces
a **sea breeze**.

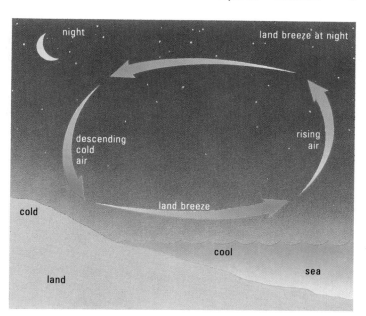

Figure 5
At night, the sea is hotter than the land.

Ocean currents also affect air temperatures and so make a difference to atmospheric circulation. For example, Britain is much warmer than many other places on the same latitude because warm water from the Tropics, called the **North Atlantic Drift**, flows up the west coast. Places near the sea experience much less extreme ranges of temperature (the Maritime Effect) than those in the centre of continents (the Continental Effect).

Place	England (0°)	Central Russia (85° E)	China/Russia border (120° E)	East Canada (70° W)
Month				
January	5	−20	−30	−20
April	10	0	0	0
July	15	15	15	15
October	10	0	−5	5

Average temperatures at places at different longitudes on latitude 53° N, in °C

6 Use an atlas to look up the winter and summer temperatures at other places on the same latitude.

Ocean currents affect temperatures on shore. In winter, Fort William in Scotland has the same temperature as Bristol. Both of these places face the Atlantic and are warmer than Inverness or Margate on the east coast.

7 Draw a map of Britain. Mark on it the towns mentioned in the paragraph above and also your own town. Describe how you would expect your town to be affected by the North Atlantic Drift.

Section E1.4 Masses of air!

How the global circulation affects you

Figure 1
Warm air from the south rides over cold air from the north and makes the **Polar Front**.

In figure 3 in the last section you can see a belt of low pressure at about the latitude of Britain. This is the boundary between two large air masses: the cold, dry **Polar Continental,** and the warm, moist **Tropical Maritime** which comes from over the Atlantic. Where the air masses move together, and the warm, less dense maritime air rides over the cold Polar air, a boundary called the **Polar Front** forms. As this is near Britain, it controls most of our weather.

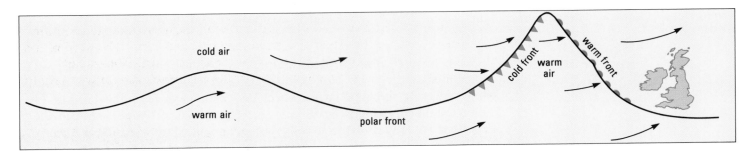

As the air masses move, kinks form in the Polar Front. At the eastern side of the kink, the warm air rides over the cold air and forms a **warm front.** Behind, to the west, cold air pushes under the warm air and forms a **cold front.** The two fronts are quite different, and not just mirror images.

At the apex the kink deepens and a centre of low pressure forms. Figure 2 is a plan view of a typical low (or **depression**) moving towards Britain from the south-west, figure 3 a section from the ocean liner *QEII* to London.

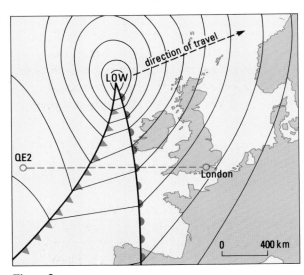

Figure 2
A low moving towards Britain.

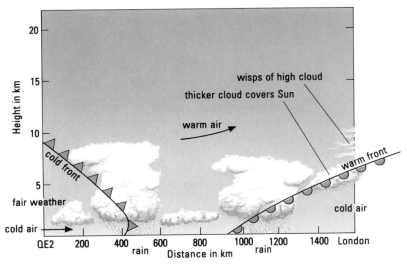

Figure 3
A vertical section through the low shown in figure 2.

Look at figures 2 and 3 and compare them with the story of what happened as the weather moved eastwards; notice the distance scale.

18:00	Cirrus cloud; pressure falling; light south to south-west wind. Following the cirrus, medium alto-stratus cloud covers the sky. Wind increasing and cloud thickening.
00:00	Drizzle from thicker cloud turning to heavier, steady rain from line of cumulus cloud as front approaches. Pressure still falling.
05:00	**WARM FRONT PASSES**: Pressure becomes steady; temperature rises a few degrees; low clouds cover sky, some light rain or drizzle; wind veers from south-west to west. Conditions continue as warm sector passes until about 15.00.
15:00	Rain begins to fall more heavily.
17:30	**COLD FRONT PASSES**: Very heavy rain from cumulo-nimbus cloud; strong gusty wind veering sharply from west to between north-west and north. Temperature drops by about 5 °C. Pressure rises and cold front sky clears to give a cold, sunny day with good visibility and occasional showers from isolated cumulus clouds.

Note how the wind veers at each front. ('Veer' means to change direction clockwise, 'back' means to change direction anti-clockwise.) The wind blows in the direction shown by the arrows, nearly parallel to the isobars but angled in slightly towards the low. This makes an anti-clockwise spiral round the low.

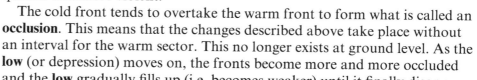

1 How long did it take for the whole depression to pass overhead?

2 What weather came as the warm front passed? What came with the cold front?

Isobars are lines of equal atmospheric pressure, i.e. pressure contours. Usually each isobar is marked with its pressure in millibars. The closer they are together the steeper the pressure gradient (the more rapid the pressure change), and the stronger the wind. The boundary between the air-masses is steeper at a cold front than a warm front, so that weather changes are quicker and more violent.

The cold front tends to overtake the warm front to form what is called an **occlusion**. This means that the changes described above take place without an interval for the warm sector. This no longer exists at ground level. As the **low** (or depression) moves on, the fronts become more and more occluded and the **low** gradually fills up (i.e. becomes weaker) until it finally disappears.

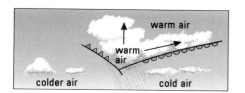

Figure 4
When the cold front overtakes the warm front, an **occlusion** is formed.

3 Find out (or work out) how an occlusion will be visible.

Sometimes a **high**, a region of high pressure where air is sinking from the upper levels of the atmosphere, is called an **anticyclone**. Those that affect Britain usually occur either south of the Polar Front in summer, bringing good sunny warm weather, or north of the Polar Front in winter. Then they give clear sunny days but very cold temperatures, especially at night, often with severe frosts. As the air is descending it is being compressed and getting

Figure 5a
Thread-like cirrus clouds, like those in figure 6 on page 6, show the approach of a warm front. High clouds increase while lower cumulus clouds disperse.

Figure 5b
There is now a layer of cirrostratus with a halo round the sun. This is one of the more definite signs of the approach of bad weather, associated with a depression.

Figure 5c
The clouds have lowered to thin altostratus with a 'watery' sun; rain will soon begin.

Figure 5d
The cloud has become thick altostratus to windward, moving slowly with rain.

Figure 5e
Thick altostratus covers the sky and continuous rain falls till the front passes, perhaps for a few hours. When the front has passed, the higher clouds disperse, the rain ceases, but fog and low stratus are likely till the cold front brings colder, drier air and clearing skies.

slightly warmer, so stable clear conditions are produced and only light winds. Highs often stay put for several days or even longer, blocking off the arrival of depressions from the west.

Warm fronts are shown on weather maps by lines which have rounded blobs on their leading edge; cold fronts have pointed blobs or 'teeth'.

4 Collect the weather maps from a daily paper. Use them to follow the weather as warm and cold fronts cross the place where you live.

5 Which way do winds blow around a low; which way around a high?

Figure 6a
At the approach of a cold front the sky will become overcast, with towering cumulus and cumulonimbus clouds giving heavy rain or snow showers.

Figure 6b
The frontal rain seldom lasts long, and as the skies break you can see the towering cumulonimbus clouds which give the heavy showers.

Figure 6c
The sky will usually clear for a time but it will not be long before the first cumulus clouds begin to form.

Topic **E2**   **Geology**

Section E2.1   Finding minerals

Mining used to be essential to Britain's economy. When transport was difficult, most minerals that technologists wanted to use had to be mined here. Salt was mined in Cheshire. Copper and tin were mined in Cornwall. The industrial revolution depended on iron ore and coal from the Midlands. Nowadays large ships can carry minerals to us from anywhere in the world, but mining is still important for our economy.

1 What other minerals are essential for life today? Make a list.

Even the simple life needs minerals from the ground. Stone buildings need quarries for the stone and for the limestone that makes mortar to hold the stones together. Cups, plates and pots need clay, and glass bottles need sand. Even today, most of these minerals that we use are mined in Britain.

2 Find out which minerals are plentiful and which are in short supply.

Some minerals are common; you can find them in most places. Other minerals are rarer and geologists are always looking for new sources. Today's big shortage is of fuels, mainly oil and gas, which are used to power our industries.

The search for minerals has been closely associated with the science of Geology. As miners have found more deposits of different minerals, geologists have built up a knowledge of our world and have developed theories about how it has come to be like it is. Here are some of the theories.

All at sea

3 Think about the part of Britain in which you live. Describe what it might have been like a thousand years ago. Do the same for ten thousand years ago, then much longer before that.

Would it surprise you if it were suggested that where you are now used to be at the bottom of a tropical sea? You might recognize some fish and other sea creatures but there might also be some which would be unfamiliar. Instead of sitting (or swimming) at latitude 56° N, you might be quite close to the Equator. How can anyone think such a thing?

Figure 1
Fossilized ripple marks in sandstone near Thurso, in Scotland.

Figure 2
Fossilized dune bedding in Devon.

Figure 3
Warm-sea fossils from Shropshire.

By looking at the rocks and minerals in Britain and examining them carefully, geologists have been able to construct a story of the formation of the land on which we live. The rocks and mineral resources which now form part of the landscape provide information for theories about how the Earth used to be.

If Britain used to be under the sea, you would expect sediment and salt water, and this is just what you can find. In Cheshire, salts are mined from beneath the ground. These salts are mainly chlorides of sodium and potassium. They now occur as crystalline deposits several metres thick, as if they were once dissolved in a sea which slowly evaporated in a hot climate. As the water evaporated, salts gradually came out and were later covered by sediment which eventually became rock.

Nearby is red sandstone. How it formed is shown by the patterns in its surface. These patterns are just like those that wind produces on desert sand. Evidence that the sand formed in dunes is given by the layers piled up when the wind blew strongly. The direction of the prevailing wind can be worked out from the direction of the layers within the dunes. This suggests that the dunes were at a latitude 15° north of the Equator. Ripple marks in other sandstone are like the ripples you can see in sand at the edge of the sea. It is evidence that this sand began its existence in shallow water.

Perhaps a coral reef would be an obvious accompaniment to sea and sand, and there is evidence for this, too. Coral reefs are made of the outside skeletons of small marine animals. Coral is made of calcium carbonate, just like the limestone that is abundant in Britain. British limestone contains fossils of animals which needed a warm, shallow, tropical sea. Limestone is mainly used in road construction and in making cement, but it is also important in agriculture and for use in the chemical industry.

Coal occurs in many parts of Britain. It contains evidence that our climate used to be very different. Coal contains fossils from tree-sized plants which grew in hot, wet conditions rather like a modern tropical rain forest.

4 Find out what minerals are mined in your area.

Figure 4
Opencast coal mining in Northumberland.

Restless Earth

You may know how devastating a volcano can be. Figures 1 and 2 on page 27 show the destruction of Mount St Helens by a single powerful eruption. There are no active volcanoes in Britain today, but you can find signs that they once existed here, because volcanic rocks occur in many places.

Figure 5
Edinburgh castle is built on an old volcano.

You would expect to find sea sediments on the plains, but you can also find them on mountain-tops. Both Leonardo da Vinci and Charles Darwin noticed fossilized sea shells in rocks hundreds of metres above sea level.

5 Suggest two different theories to explain why there are sea sediments and fossils on mountain-tops.

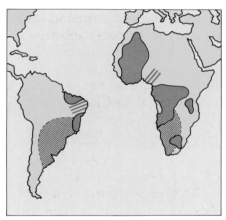

//// distribution of fossil reptile *Mesosaurus*

▓▓ similar types of rock

≡≡ folds in rock

Figure 6
Can you explain the patterns of rock type and the fossil distribution?

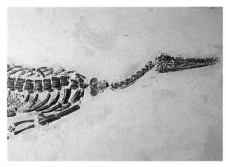

Figure 7
A Mesosaurus fossil.

Many rocks of Britain could not have built up in a sea or in a desert. The Pennine and Snowdon mountain ranges look like pushed-up regions of ground. If this process happened after sand was laid down, the sand would be lifted as the mountain rose. This would explain how sediment could end up on mountain-tops. Evidence like this leads geologists to think that the Earth is on the move and that earth movements of the kind that generate earthquakes have caused rocks to be uplifted, folded and generally distorted.

There is evidence of even more movement of the Earth. Geologists noticed that the mineral map of Africa is very similar to the mineral map of South America. Not only do the minerals match (that may be a coincidence), but fossils found in the two areas also match. It is as if Africa and South America were once joined up. Volcanoes erupting and mountains being pushed up suggest that parts of the Earth are moving. Perhaps whole continents can move around.

Section E2.2 The moving Earth

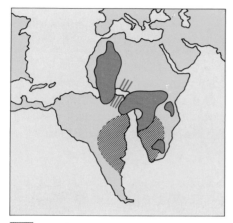

distribution of fossil reptile *Mesosaurus*

similar types of rock

folds in rock

Figure 1
If you fit South America and Africa together, the rock and fossil distributions are easy to understand.

In the last section, you learned that fossils and mineral deposits show how similar the geology in parts of Africa is to that of South America. Before trying to understand that, think about another observation of our Earth.

If you look at figure 1, you can see from their shapes that Africa and South America could have fitted together. This is not a new idea: the English scientist Francis Bacon noticed it in 1620.

1 Suggest a theory to explain why the shapes of the Earth's continents fit together.

In 1912, the German scientist Alfred Wegener suggested that all the World's continents were once a single block that has now drifted apart. But he could not explain how they moved and few scientists believed him. Since then several different scientific observations have given support to his theory.

Mountains under the sea

Geologists study the floor of the oceans, as well as what is visible on land. You might expect the oceans to be shallow at the sides and deepest in the middle. But under the sea, in the middle of the Atlantic Ocean, there is a ridge of mountains up to 3 kilometres high. There are volcanoes at different places down the ridge. At the north of the ridge the volcanoes are most active. The ridge is high enough there to be above sea level. This is Iceland.

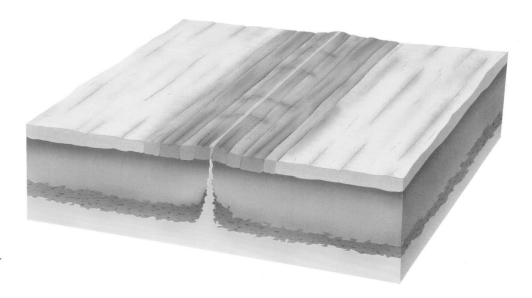

Figure 2
A cross-section of the ridge down the floor of the Atlantic Ocean.

2 What other ridges and trenches are there in the oceans? Use an atlas to find out.

Geologists use maps of the ocean floor to see how well the continents fit together at different depths below the sea, as well as at the surface. This can allow for the continental shelf – a platform around the continent which is an extension of the land, but now under the sea. These tests also show that the continents fit together well.

Magnetic evidence

If you have used a map and a compass together, you know that magnetic north is not in the same place as true north. Not only is there a difference but it changes from year to year. A 1935 map stated that magnetic north was 11° west of true north, but a 1989 map stated that magnetic north was about 5° west of true north.

3 How much had the magnetic field moved from 1935 to 1989? How long at that rate would it take for the magnetic field to change by 180°?

It is easy to work out how fast the Earth's magnetic field changes during the periods that scientists have been taking measurements. We have to make theories about what happened before this with evidence from magnetic minerals.

Many minerals are magnetic, especially those which contain iron. When volcanic rock solidifies in the Earth's magnetic field, its minerals take on the Earth's magnetism. This produces magnetic 'fossils' which show the angle between the Earth's field and the solidifying minerals. There are iron mineral deposits in the Lake District. In these, the magnetic field shows that the magnetic Pole was south of where Britain is today. But in other areas, the field direction is different. You can see that these rocks must have solidified at times when the Earth's field was in different directions, so they must have solidified at different times. Evidence like this suggests that the Earth's magnetic field has changed many times over a long period.

Magnetic evidence provides information about the relative position of the continents to the magnetic Pole when minerals solidified. It indicates that the central parts of Africa and South America, which are now near the Equator, were once close to the south magnetic Pole.

The sea floor also contains an interesting magnetic pattern. The rocks underneath the sea have strips which are magnetized in opposite directions. This means that each different strip solidified at a different time from its neighbour. The magnetic strips are mirror images of each other on either side of the mid-ocean ridges.

4 Examine the evidence for yourself. What conclusion would you draw from mineral and fossil evidence, the fit between the continents, and the mountains and magnetic strips under the sea?

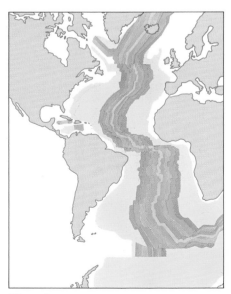

Figure 3
A magnetic map of the Atlantic Ocean.

Plate tectonics

Figure 4
Volcanic vent or 'smoker' on the Ocean floor.

Together, this evidence leads to the theory of **plate tectonics**. This states that continents were once joined together and have gradually moved around. The continents are parts of solid plates which are able to move over the interior of the Earth, like plates sliding over the surface of a table. The plates are able to move over a layer of partly molten rock underneath, sometimes joining, sometimes separating. As America moved away from Europe and Africa, molten rock pushed up in between. The molten rock solidified in stages to form the ocean floor, with its magnetic strips and mountains. Gradually the distance between the continents increased.

It is exciting that scientists can test the theory of plate tectonics. Radio telescopes and laser rangefinding equipment show that the continents are still moving. Europe and Africa are moving away from North and South America at a few centimetres per year.

5 The distance between Africa and South America is about 4000 km. If they drifted apart at a steady 4 cm per year, how long ago were they touching?

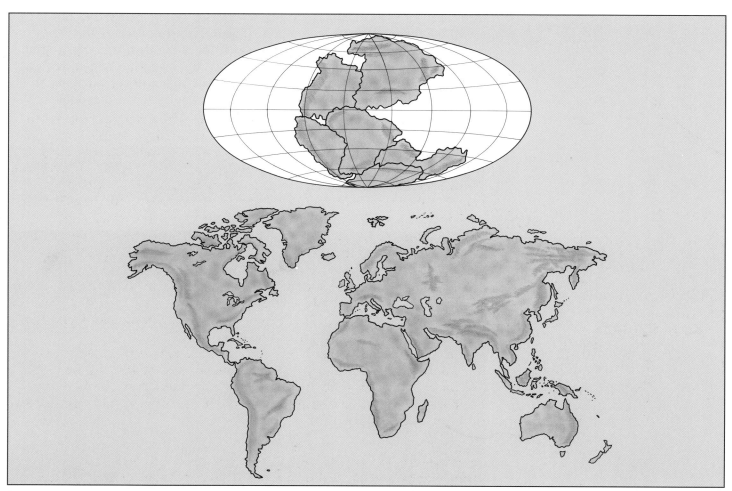

Figure 5
'Pangea', how the Earth's continents used to be, and how they are today.

Section E2.3   Earthquakes

There is more to plate tectonics than continents moving apart. If plates move apart in one place, then in other places they must be moving together. Edges between plates are called **plate margins**. At some plate margins, long chains of mountains are produced. The Scottish Highlands are one chain. A bigger chain is the Alpine-Himalayan chain which extends from southern Europe, across the Middle East to India.

> **1** Use an atlas to find the Alpine-Himalayan chain. What other chains of mountains can you find?

Piled-up crust becomes hot because work has been done on it. So hot water solutions containing precious minerals rise up and penetrate cracks in the rocks. They leave mineral deposits when they cool. This shows how useful the theory of plate tectonics is. If geologists know where the plate margins are, they can predict where to look for minerals within the ground. Plate margins in Britain have veins of copper, tin, lead, tungsten and other ores. Most of these have now been dug out, but higher prices can make it economic to reopen old mines, such as that in Anglesey which produces copper, lead and zinc ores, plus some silver and gold.

> **2** Use an atlas to find where in the World copper is mined. What patterns do you notice about these places?

Figure 1
Copper mining in Anglesey.

Violent movements

What would you expect when vast amounts of the Earth's surface move around, even though it happens slowly? As anyone who has observed an earthquake knows, the effects can be loud and violent. Earthquakes occur when stresses which have built up in the ground are suddenly released. The result is often devastating, resulting in avalanches, tidal waves, destruction of homes, and the deaths of humans and animals.

Some earthquakes occur at plate margins where plates are scraping past each other on a 'fault'. San Francisco sits on the San Andreas fault. Residents of San Francisco must wonder when the next earthquake will occur. Other earthquakes occur at margins where plates are descending into the mantle.

Geologists would like to be able to predict earthquakes and have made some progress in that direction. There are hundreds of stations around the globe picking up earthquake waves and adding to the information about where the earthquake starts and what might cause it.

The apparatus used to pick up earthquake waves is called a seismometer. This consists of a mass suspended by a spring inside a frame. When an earthquake occurs, the frame, which is attached to the ground, moves. The suspended mass stays in the same place. So the spring responds to earthquake waves by changing length. A paper or magnetic tape records the movement. Earthquakes produce different types of waves. Studying these waves gives seismologists information about the structure of the Earth.

3 Where would be a bad place to put a seismic station? (Hint: seismometers pick up all sorts of vibrations.)

Figure 2
Earthquake damage in Mexico City, September 1985.

Figure 3
A car caught up in the last serious San Francisco earthquake.

Figure 4
A seismologist checking seismometer equipment.

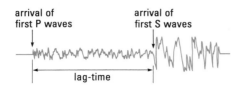

Figure 5
P waves and S waves recorded by a seismometer.

P waves are longitudinal, or compression, waves. The material through which the waves travel is compressed and then stretched. P waves can travel through both solids and liquids. S waves are transverse waves and travel by vibrating from side to side at right angles to the direction of travel of the wave. They can only be transmitted through solids.

> **4** Both P and S waves can travel through the outside of the Earth, the **crust**. But S waves cannot travel through the centre of the Earth, the **core**. What does this tell you about the crust and the core?
>
> **5** Draw a diagram to show the difference between a longitudinal wave, like a P wave, and a transverse wave, like an S wave.

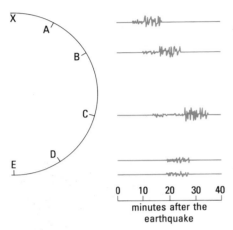

Figure 6
Waves from an earthquake at x, recorded by different seismometers around the world.

There are two other types of waves known as Rayleigh and Love waves. They cause the greatest damage, because they travel slowly along the surface with a rolling motion.

P waves in the Earth's interior travel faster than S waves, so they arrive first. The seismometer records the interval, or **lag-time**, between the arrival of P and S waves, and this information is useful in locating where the earthquake started. If the lag-times from three seismometers in three different locations are known, the exact position of the earthquake's starting point can be located.

Earthquake waves have provided valuable information about the structure of the Earth. Waves from the same earthquake are picked up at different recording stations around the world. Figure 6 shows the different wave forms arriving at various stations. The paths of waves arriving at the stations are not straight lines but curves. This is because the waves change speed and direction as they encounter material of different stiffness and density in the Earth's interior.

> **6** What name do scientists use for waves changing speed and direction? Give an example of another wave that does this.

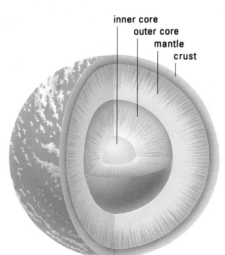

Crust   Thickness 5–75 km   Density 2700–3000 kg/m^3
Mantle Thickness 2900 km   Density 3000–5500kg/m^3
Core   radius 3500 km   Density 10 000–12 500kg/m^3

Figure 7
Inside the Earth.

At D and E there are no S waves as the waves have had to travel through the core. This suggests that the core contains liquid which does not transmit these waves. Evidence from waves has led to a picture of the Earth's interior in three main layers: core, mantle and crust. The crust is solid, the mantle is a mixture of solid and liquid, and the outer core is liquid. Scientists think that the inner core is solid. This explains how the continents are able to move. The solid plates of crust move on the partly molten mantle.

To measure the thickness of the Earth's crust, scientists can make their own earthquakes by setting off explosives and picking up reflected sound waves. These measurements can also give us information about the properties of different parts of the Earth. They show that the Earth's solid crust varies from 6 or 7 km thick under the sea to more than 30 km thick beneath the continents. Underneath is the mantle in a whole series of layers with differing densities. The mantle is made of denser rock than the crust; it has more iron and magnesium in it. Density measurement has led to the conclusion that the core is made mainly of iron.

Section E2.4   Recycled rocks!

Three kinds of rocks

Volcanoes produce some of the strongest rocks. Minerals which have been heated inside them at great pressure and then allowed to cool, produce materials like granite and basalt. Rocks like these are called **igneous** rocks from the Latin for **fire**. Not all igneous rocks come from volcanoes but all igneous rocks show signs of being formed at high temperature. Igneous rocks are being made all the time in the crust and the outer mantle.

Figure 1
Lava flowing from an erupting volcano in Hawaii.

Even though we are mortal, we may want our gravestones to last a long time. An igneous rock is the best choice. Granite building stones will outlast any other material. But, hard though granite is, a granite mountain is not indestructible. Gradually it gets broken down. This process is called **weathering**. The most important agent in weathering is water.

Physical weathering breaks down the rock into smaller pieces of the same type of rock. Water gets into tiny cracks in rock and then expands when it freezes. This forces the rock apart. Tiny fragments or huge pieces of rock can be pushed off in this way. In **chemical weathering**, the chemical structure of a rock is changed to form a new mineral. Water dissolves part of the rock, so that the remaining mineral is chemically different and is no longer held together.

1 Look round a graveyard. Describe the stones which have lasted well and those which have weathered badly.

Figure 2
A tree growing in rock in California.

Biological action causes both physical and chemical weathering. Plant roots can get into cracks and split rocks. Small organisms can attack the rock chemically. Recently man's own actions have contributed to weathering. Acid rain in particular increases the rate of chemical weathering.

2 Man-made materials weather as well as rocks. Describe some weathering of a man-made material that you have seen.

After weathering, various **slope processes** cause rock to move from upland areas down into river and glacier valleys. Landslips and landslides can be dramatic, but the steady creep of soil down a slope is important in getting weathered material downhill.

Finally **erosion** occurs, which wears away and removes weathered material. Winds can blow debris, particularly fine sand, in deserts or at the sea shore. But you may have guessed that water is again the most important agent in erosion. Glaciers are huge rivers of ice. They can move everything from dust to boulders as big as houses. Rivers can wash away huge quantities of sediment, especially when they are in flood. Tides and storms at sea move sand and rocks along the coast. Eventually, even the strongest mountain rock material ends as sediment at the bottom of a lake or sea.

3 What happens to this sediment when it is left long enough?

On page 15 you read about the rocks sandstone and limestone. These are called **sedimentary** rocks because they are made of sediment, material that

Figure 3
An advancing glacier in Alaska.

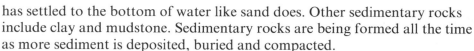

Figure 4
A river in flood in England.

has settled to the bottom of water like sand does. Other sedimentary rocks include clay and mudstone. Sedimentary rocks are being formed all the time as more sediment is deposited, buried and compacted.

There is one other group of rocks which are called **metamorphic**. This word means 'changing form'. Metamorphic rocks form when sedimentary rocks are pressed together at plate margins. High temperatures and enormous pressures change the minerals in sedimentary rocks to new ones with different structures. Slate, schist and gneiss are the commonest metamorphic rocks in Britain. They are found in the north-west of Britain. You will not be surprised to know that metamorphic rocks are also being formed all the time in the Earth's crust.

As rocks are pushed by continuing plate movement, they often end up under the ground again, where the temperatures are high enough to turn them back into igneous rocks. What a long journey it is from igneous to sedimentary to metamorphic and finally back to igneous. This process is continuing all the time. It is called the **rock cycle**.

4 What rocks are found in your area? Use the map on page 26 to find out.

Power for the rock cycle

Churning the Earth's rocks around like this is a process that needs a huge power supply whose source is hidden in the ground. As you go down into the Earth it gets hotter. The increase in temperature for each kilometre increase in depth is called the **geothermal gradient**. It depends on local conditions. In a region of active volcanoes, for instance, the gradient will be high. In Britain, the average gradient is 30 °C per kilometre. Where there is a mass of granite beneath the surface the geothermal gradient is nearer 50 °C per kilometre. Granite contains radioactive minerals. As the minerals decay they release energy and heat the rocks.

No one knows how much radioactivity there is in the Earth, but the heating effect is well known. In Cornwall engineers have built a **geothermal** power station. They have drilled holes six kilometres deep and shattered the rock at the bottom with explosives. Cold water is pumped down one hole and hot water under pressure comes up the other hole. This drives turbines and generates electricity. Most geothermal stations are in parts of the World with higher geothermal gradients than Britain, such as Iceland.

Figure 5
A geothermal power station in Iceland.

5 What are the best rocks for geothermal power stations? Use the map on page 26 to find where these rocks are in Britain.

Geothermal electricity generators are a new idea, but for thousands of years man has used natural hot springs coming out of the ground as a source of heating. For very much longer, the same source of power has been powering the rock cycle. Is it surprising to realize that all these processes rely on the natural nuclear power station inside the earth?

GEOLOGY IN BRITAIN

Boulders of Lewisian gneiss on a beach on Lewis, Scotland.

Limestone pavement near Malham tarn, Yorkshire.

Coniston slate from the Lake District, being cut.

Bedded sandstone from Ashford, Kent.

Key
- sedimentary
- low temperature metamorphic
- high temperature metamorphic
- igneous

Pillow lava from Newborough Warren, Anglesey.

Pink feldspar granite from Dartmoor.

Section E2.5   How fast does it happen?

Figure 1
Mount St Helens before the eruption.

Figure 2
Mount St Helens after the eruption.

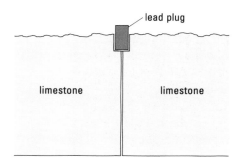

Figure 3
Limestone blocks in St Paul's cathedral wear away much faster than the lead plugs in them.

Earth scientists study processes which happened long before mankind started recording information. So they work out from present observations what happened in the past.

In order to make theories about what happened in the past, scientists use the **principle of uniformity**. This principle states that things in the past happen in just the same way as things we observe happening today. The principle of uniformity is an assumption: it is something that scientists accept without proof. But without the principle, there would be no way to start Earth Science. You used the principle of uniformity if you answered questions **3** and **5** on pages 18 and 19.

1 When do you use the principle of uniformity? What would life be like without it?

Geologists work 'in the field' making observations on existing rocks. They try to observe stages in the rock cycle where this is possible. Then they make theories assuming that the way rocks are forming now is the way they have always formed. Some changes are slow and difficult to observe and measure. Other changes occur suddenly. When a volcano erupts, in a day or less the landscape can be transformed and millions of tonnes of rock be deposited on the Earth's surface.

Weathering and erosion

Weathering and erosion generally happen at a steady pace, though occasionally there are sudden bursts. Some rocks which are exposed at the surface have not changed much in thousands of years. This means that they bear evidence for what happened in the past. For example, some rocks in Britain bear huge scratches. Earth scientists deduce that these scratches were caused by rocks at the base of a moving ice sheet during the last Ice Age.

Weathering of man-made structures can be like weathering that takes place in nature. Parts of St Paul's cathedral in London are made of limestone held together with lead plugs. The limestone has weathered at about a tenth of a millimetre per year, but the lead plugs have hardly weathered at all. Once the plugs were level with the surface, but now the plugs stand about 2 cm above the surrounding limestone.

2 Use the figures in the above paragraph to estimate the age of St Paul's cathedral.

Figure 4
A block of sandstone deposited on a limestone pavement on the slopes of Ingleborough in Yorkshire.

Figure 4 shows a block of sandstone left behind long ago on the surrounding limestone by an ice sheet. Limestone underneath the stone has been protected from erosion by the sandstone, while the rest of the limestone has been weathered away. This leaves the sandstone on a low pedestal of limestone about 30 cm high.

---

3 The limestone is now weathering away at about 0.03 mm per year. At that rate, how long ago was the sandstone level with the limestone surrounding it? Give a reason why this rate of weathering is slower than the weathering of St Paul's cathedral.

Sometimes erosion occurs quickly. Cliffs on the Yorkshire coast are being rapidly washed away so that whole villages have disappeared. But the damage is mainly done when there is a sudden violent storm and large chunks of the cliff disappear. On average a metre of cliff disappears each year. Comparing an old map with a modern one is a good way to see how the coastline has changed.

Off the coast of Lincolnshire, in an area north of the Wash, land is being added constantly. The mud which is added comes in from the sea. The fine particles are in suspension in the water and after each high tide a thin layer a few thousandths of a millimetre thick is left behind. Families of farmers who own this land are fortunate. If they own a good stretch of land along the coastline they can gain several extra acres in a century.

A slower process is the build-up of limestone. Some of the living things which eventually form part of limestone can be seen in a coral reef. Corals and other animals which are attached to the reef have skeletons of calcium carbonate. As they grow their skeleton grows, and when they die the skeleton is left behind. These skeletons and other shells form the basis of a deposit which eventually becomes limestone. Now limestones can be seen to form cliffs hundreds of metres high, such as in the Dolomites in northern Italy.

4 Coral reefs in the Pacific can grow by 2 cm per year. How long would it take to make a cliff 70 m high like those in the Avon Gorge?

There are some very high mountains in the world, and some of them are still getting higher. The mountain-building process can be seen in areas where earthquakes occur frequently. California is one such place. The changes in height are so great that they show up if you compare a map of 100 years ago with a modern map. At this rate of uplift, in two million years there will be a range of mountains higher than the Himalayas are today.

5 The land in California is rising by 5 mm per year. How much lower was it 100 years ago? How high will it be if it keeps on rising at the same rate for two million years? Compare your answer with the height of the Himalayas.

Fast erosion

Fast and dramatic changes are not observed now and it is hard to be sure what part they played in making our landscape. In the Yorkshire Moors is a valley which seems to have been formed very quickly. Newton Dale is 6 km long. It has a broad flat floor about 200 m wide with steep sides 100 m high (page 13). Scientists think that it may have been formed in as little as twenty years, with vast flows of water, ten times faster than the Thames in flood. This water probably came from a rapidly melting glacier. This is a reminder that fast processes may have caused some old landforms.

Mankind's own activities can cause changes very rapidly. Much of the Aral Sea, which is on the border between Uzbekistan and Kazakhstan, has dried up in the last twenty years as engineers have diverted water from rivers that supply it and used the water for artificial irrigation. In a similar way, commercial peat extraction has removed most of the peat bogs from Britain. This has removed the habitat of many plant and animal species.

Figure 5
The Aral Sea after diversion of the rivers which once fed it.

Figure 6
A peat bog in Ireland.

Section E2.6   Geological time

If you are near an earthquake, it may seem that geological processes can be very quick. Fast processes, like the one which formed Newton Dale (page 13), may have been at work in the past. But on the scale of the Earth, even the largest earthquake or the largest volcanic eruption has only a small effect. If we wanted to see a large mountain range forming, or a similar range being weathered and eroded away, we would have to wait a very long time at the present rate at which these things happen.

> **1** Collect together your answers to question **5** on page 19 and questions **3** to **5** on pages 28 and 29. From these figures, how old would you say that the Earth is?

In some of the questions that you have answered, you have used the principle of uniformity to calculate the times for some geological processes. One of the first scientists to do this was a geologist named James Hutton (1726–97). He used the principle of uniformity to work out a figure for the age of the Earth. Scientists use similar principles today. From these methods they deduce that, if things in the past happened at the same rate as they do today, the Earth cannot be less than 4500 million years old.

Since our own life span is only about 70 years, it is hard to imagine such a long time. And even the longest estimates of the time that man has been around on the Earth are small compared with this.

Figure 1
Annual glacial sediment layers in a lake bed.

In the questions you have answered, you have already used the thickness of sediments to measure geological time. This is only reliable if the rates of sedimentation are constant. Sometimes sediments are deposited in yearly layers, so the age can be worked out by counting them. In Scandinavian lakes there are layered deposits from ice sheets. Each spring and summer the ice melted and left a deposit. Coarser material settled to the bottom first and finer material later in the year. When the ice froze again, only fine material continued to settle. The process repeated itself each year and the layers can easily be counted, rather like counting growth rings in a tree.

Radioactive dating

You might have heard about the use of carbon-14 dating to estimate the ages of objects made of materials that used to be alive. There is a small amount of the isotope carbon-14 in the atmosphere along with the more common carbon-12. Carbon-14 decays, but living materials keep on taking in more as they grow and so have a constant proportion. When death occurs, there is no replacement of carbon-14, so the proportion decreases. The half-life of carbon-14 is only 5570 years, so this method is useful to date plants and animals which might have lived thousands of years ago but not millions.

2 What fraction of the original carbon-14 will be left in a sample that died 11 140 years ago? Explain why carbon-14 dating does not work on a sample that is 55 700 years old.

A similar method is used to date minerals in the Earth. You read on page 25 that within the Earth is a natural nuclear power station. Not all minerals

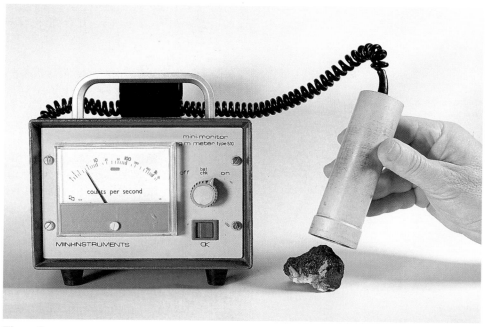

Figure 2
Detecting radioactivity in a mineral.

are radioactive but many contain tiny amounts of radioactive elements. The most accurate estimates of the ages of rocks make use of that radioactivity.

If a rock is liquid or in solution it can gain or lose elements. But once a mineral becomes solid, the elements that make it up can only change as a result of radioactive decay. Uranium-238 is a common radioactive element in the Earth's crust. It decays to lead. If a mineral contains uranium, this will decay and gradually increase the amount of lead in that mineral. From the ratio of uranium to lead, scientists can estimate how long ago the rock solidified, if they assume certain proportions for how much lead was there at the beginning.

Figure 3
Even common minerals like these contain trace radioactive elements.

A very slow change in potassium happens when a proton in the nucleus captures an electron from the outer shell. The result is an atom of argon. The half-life for this is 11 850 million years. The method described above can thus also be used to date a rock by measuring the ratio of argon to potassium.

3 Imagine a mountain range like the Pennines. Which rocks would you expect to have solidified first, those at the top or those at the bottom? Explain your answer.

Both radioactive measurements mentioned, and others like them, have been used to date a wide variety of rocks. Many of the results are what you might expect. Rock from the top of mountains shows a greater age than rock from the bottom. This is consistent with the idea that the mountains are made from pushed-up rock. The rocks at the top show a greater age because they solidified first.

Scientists use a mass spectrometer to measure the proportion of different isotopes in a sample. First they heat the sample to make a vapour. Then fast electrons bombard the vapour in a vacuum chamber. This knocks electrons off atoms in the sample and creates positive ions. Then an electric field accelerates the ions; a magnetic field then deflects them. The amount of deflection depends on the mass of the ions. A detector measures the quantity of each isotope as well as the type.

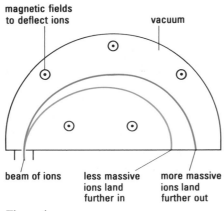

Figure 4
The magnetic field in a **mass spectrometer** deflects different ions by different amounts.

Matching fossils

Once rocks have been dated by one method or another, scientists can then use fossils to compare these rocks with samples which they cannot date by other methods. If they find a rock containing fossils, they assume that it is the same age as another rock containing the same fossils. The most useful fossils for this purpose are those which moved freely in the seas, and so are widely distributed across the Earth. The fossils must also be found in a variety of rock types and show wide evolutionary changes. The basic idea for this matching is that a particular evolutionary form of an organism occurs throughout the world at only one time. When it becomes extinct, it will not reappear.

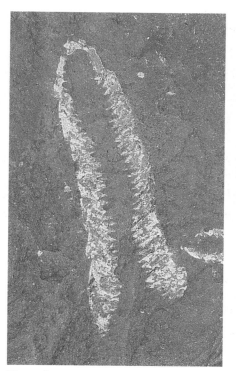

Figure 5
Fossil graptolite (*Didymograptus murchisoni*)

Figure 6
Fossil ammonites (*Echioceras raricostratum*)

4 The Thanet sands in Kent have been dated at 57 million years old using potassium/argon dating. There are other sands in Surrey dated at 115 million years old. If you had field trips to see these two types of sand, what other differences between them would you look for?

With all these methods, Earth scientists have built up a picture of the vast span of geological time. This is shown on the chart on the next page.

5 Compare your estimate of the age of the Earth from question **1** with the time chart on the next page. What conclusion do you draw from the comparison?

GEOLOGICAL TIME CHART

Geologists divide time into three **eras**, according to the type of fossil found in them. The most recent era is called **Cainozoic** (new animals). Before that is **Mesozoic** (middle animals). Older than that are **Palaeozoic** (old animals) and **Precambrian** (before Cambrian, the earliest period of Palaeozoic).

The eras are divided into **periods**, and the periods divided further into **epochs**.

The time scale will probably only remain valid for a few years. Scientists keep trying to improve the way that they measure. Also, geologists may find fresh evidence for the boundaries between the different periods. This evidence from the rocks themselves may result in the boundaries being moved up or down the column by a few million years or so.

Divisions of geological time			Commencement date in millions of years
Era	**Period**	**Epoch**	
Cainozoic	Quaternary	Pleistocene	1.6
	Tertiary	Pliocene	5
		Miocene	24
		Oligocene	37
		Eocene	58
		Palaeocene	65
Mesozoic	Cretaceous		135
	Jurassic		205
	Triassic		250
Palaeozoic	Permian		290
	Carboniferous		355
	Devonian		405
	Silurian		435
	Ordovician		510
	Cambrian		570
Precambrian	Formation of the Earth		about 4600

Topic **E3**   **Space**

Section **E**3.1   **Gravity all around**

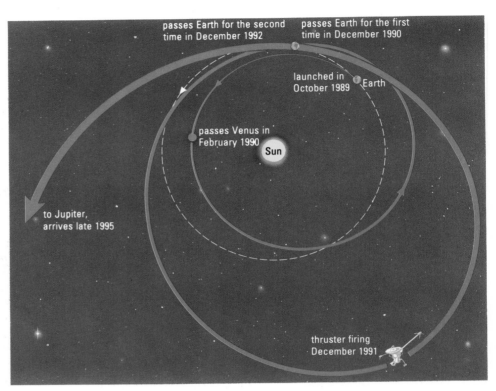

Figure 1
The path of the probe 'Galileo' on its way to Jupiter.

The space probe Galileo, launched in 1990, set off for Jupiter with a lander and an orbiter vehicle. But its course was anything but a direct one. It went around Venus, back for two orbits of Earth and then on to Jupiter. Mariner 10 made three orbits of Mercury and one around the far side of the Sun during its mission. Why are space journeys so difficult? What forces act on the space probe during its journey? How big does the rocket need to be and how fast must it go? Space travel is fascinating, but it is a complicated subject. To understand it you first need to learn about **gravity**.

If you weigh a 1-kilogram mass you find that it has a weight of nearly 10 newtons. A 2-kilogram mass has a weight of 20 newtons. But have you ever wondered why objects have weight? Objects on Earth have weight because of the Earth's gravity. The Earth pulls down on each kilogram with a force of nearly 10 newtons. Scientists say that the **gravitational field strength** at the Earth's surface is 10 newtons per kilogram. It is the pull of the Earth on an object that they call weight. Other planets have gravitational fields too.

Figure 2
You can tell the strength of the gravitational field on any planet by finding the weight of 1 kilogram.

1 What is your mass? What is your weight on Earth?

Figure 3
A falling apple gave Newton ideas about gravity!

It is said that Sir Isaac Newton was sitting near an apple tree when he thought up his theory of gravity. As he saw an apple fall, he asked himself why it was falling. A falling apple was not the only thing that was puzzling him. At the same time he was trying to work out why planets go round the Sun. Together, these questions prompted him to suggest his **universal law of gravitation**. You may think that it was easy to suggest that the Earth pulls the apple down. It took Newton's genius to suggest that, at the same time, the apple was pulling the Earth up!

Newton went on to suggest that every object in the Universe attracts every other object. The apple and the Earth attract each other; the Earth and the Sun attract each other. Two tennis balls a metre apart attract each other. These **gravitational** forces 'act at a distance' without any contact between the objects.

The size of the force between any two objects depends on the mass of each object and on their distance apart. If the objects are more massive, the force is larger. If the objects are closer together, the force is larger.

2 Give two other types of force which, like gravity, act at a distance.

Going round in circles

A falling apple gets faster as it falls: it accelerates towards the ground. If you drop a cherry at the same time as an apple, it accelerates at the same rate. Masses will still fall down even if we throw them sideways at the same time that we drop them. You see a curved path.

Kick a football horizontally off a high cliff and it lands some distance away. Kick it faster and it lands further away. It has spent longer in the process of falling and so can travel further horizontally. The Earth's surface is curved and so if we kick the ball fast enough then it falls as fast as the ground curves away beneath it. The falling ball does not reach the ground; it orbits the Earth.

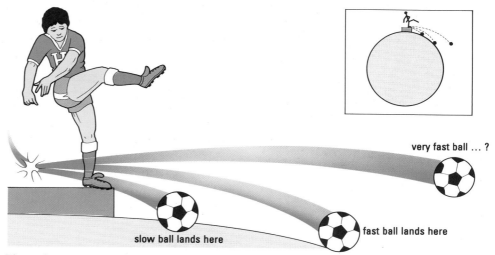

very fast ball ... ?

fast ball lands here

slow ball lands here

Figure 4
The faster you kick the football, the further it goes. But if you kick it fast enough...?

Figure 5
The Moon and the Earth pull each other like two spinning dancers.

Figure 6
The dancers keep each other going in circles by pulling hard!

The same occurs when a rocket launches a satellite. The rocket gets the satellite up to a speed of about 8 kilometres per second. The gravitational pull of the Earth on the satellite keeps the satellite falling towards the Earth in a circular path.

The Earth and the Moon exert a gravitational pull on each other. This causes the Moon to rotate around the Earth once every 28 days. In the same way there is a gravitational pull between the Earth and the Sun. This means that the Earth travels in a roughly circular path around the Sun, taking 365 days for a complete orbit. Gravitational forces between the Sun and the other planets cause their orbits too.

Orbits need not be circular. In fact most are **elliptical** (rather like a squashed circle). When the planets are close to the Sun, they travel faster than when they are further away. The elliptical orbit of Halley's comet is very **eccentric**. Most of the time it is a long way from the Sun, and hard to see from the Earth. Every 75 years it returns, loops quickly round the Sun and disappears into Space again. It last came near in 1985/6.

---

3 Give two examples of objects on Earth that go round in circles. What forces cause their circular motion?

4 Find out what the word **eccentric** means when applied to an ellipse. How else do people use the word?

5 When will Halley's comet next come back? How old will you be then? Do you think you will live long enough to see it?

Figure 7
Gravitational forces from the Sun make the planets move in their orbits.

Beyond our Solar System lies the rest of the universe. The nearest stars are vast distances away from us and most of them seem to be moving away from us. But even these distant objects are not free from the effects of gravity. Newton's law of gravity is universal. It predicts that there is a gravitational force between our Sun and these distant stars. These gravitational forces pull all the bodies in the universe together. As you will read later on page 59, this provides one of the great puzzles for today's astronomical physicists.

Section E3.2   Tides big and small

Nearly a thousand years ago, the Danish King Canute successfully took control of England. There is a story that his courtiers flattered him. They said that he was powerful enough to command the tides to stop and they would obey him. Canute was wise enough to know that tides are under no man's control.

For thousands of years people have noticed the tides. At high tide, the sea-level is at its highest and then starts to fall. Just over 6 hours later, there is low tide with the sea-level at its lowest. The water then starts to rise again to the next high tide just over 12 hours after the one before. Harbour masters need to predict the tide accurately. They reckon on 12 hours 25 minutes between each high tide, so it takes 50 minutes longer than a day for two high tides. Some tides are big, some are small. As you travel east, the tides occur earlier. Tide tables give you precise times for each tide in a particular place.

> **1** High tide is at 9 o'clock one morning. When will low tide be? When will the next high tide be?

A long time ago, people had worked out that tides keep step with the moon. Tides follow a 28-day cycle – a lunar month. But to understand why the moon is important, you need to understand gravity, the subject of the last section.

The Earth applies a gravitational pull on the Moon. In the same way, the Moon pulls on the Earth. You know that the Moon is in orbit around the Earth. Similarly the Earth is in orbit around the Moon. The two bodies are spinning around a point somewhere between their two centres like the pair of spinning dancers on page 38. It takes 28 days for a complete turn.

Figure 1
The Severn bore, a wave produced by tidal forces.

Figure 2
At high tide here in the Bay of Fundy, the boats would all be afloat.

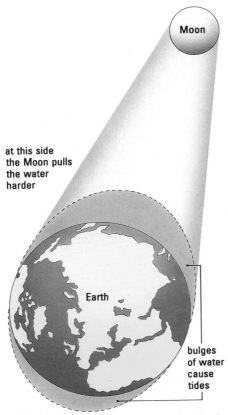

at this side
the Moon pulls
the water
harder

Moon

Earth

bulges
of water
cause
tides

at this side the Moon pulls the water less hard

Figure 3
By pulling too hard at one side and not
hard enough on the other side, the Moon
causes bulges of water on the Earth that
cause tides.

On average, the Moon provides just enough force to keep the Earth turning around the centre of rotation. But the parts of the Earth that are closest to the Moon are pulled more strongly than they need to be, and the parts of the Earth that are furthest away from the Moon are not pulled strongly enough. This causes both of these parts to bulge out, the near one towards the Moon and the far one away from the Moon. The seas bulge most, because the water in them can move easily. But the lands bulge a little as well. The Moon also distorts our atmosphere. It causes small changes in pressure in time with the tides.

At the same time as the Moon causes these bulges, the Earth is spinning on its own axis once every 24 hours. So the two bulges travel as tides over the surface of the Earth. The bulges are a little bit behind the pull, so high tide comes just after the moon is directly overhead.

2 Explain why the maximum bulge happens after the maximum pull.

The Moon is orbiting around the Earth in the same direction that the Earth is spinning. This means that it gradually falls behind, getting 24 hours behind in every 28 days. This is 50 minutes per day.

The Moon is the strongest influence on the tides. The Sun is more distant, but very much larger, and it, too, affects the tides. Its pull on the Earth is less than half that of the Moon but it is still important. Twice a month, the effects of the Sun and the Moon add up. Tides are then much larger. These are called **spring** tides. They occur when the moon appears to be full and when it is only a narrow crescent. Half-way between these times, at half moon, the effects of the Sun and the Moon partly cancel out. At these times the tides are smaller. They are called **neap** tides.

Power from the tides

If you could keep all the water that crept up our beaches twice a day, you could store a tremendous amount of energy. The dams for this salty

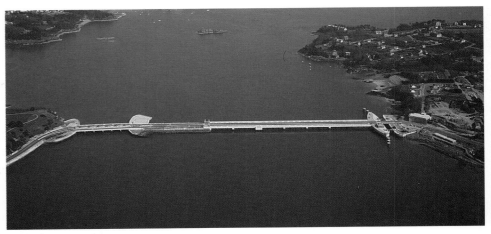

Figure 4
A tidal barrage in Brittany, France.

hydroelectric scheme would not need to be high, but they would need to be very long. Engineers have already built a tidal power station in Brittany and have developed a plan to create a dam across the estuary of the River Severn. Water would be let into the dam at high tide and then released through turbines until low tide.

> **3** If you made a tidal power station, where would the energy come from? Where would the energy go to?

You might think that tidal power like this would be friendly to the environment. But in fact the river environment would change drastically. The present tidal cycle cleans out our estuaries of sewage, sediment and industrial waste. A dam would trap these wastes, so they would gradually accumulate. The dam would keep the water higher during low tides, so the tidal mud flats would disappear, together with the wildlife that relies on the mud flats for a feeding ground. The rock and concrete needed to make it would cause massive quarrying for many miles around.

> **4** Imagine you are a civil servant advising on tidal power. Write two paragraphs to persuade the Energy Minister, first, that it is a good idea and second, that it is a bad idea.

Like a giant flywheel, the spinning Earth stores energy. Tidal power gets its energy from this store. If the Earth were not spinning, we would still have bulges on the sides nearest to and furthest from the Moon, but these bulges would stay in the same place, so they would not do work. Gradually the Earth slows down as its energy is used to power the tides. The good news is that there is a lot of energy. Every year, the slowing of the Earth increases the day by less than a hundredth of a second.

Figure 5a
The near side of the Moon

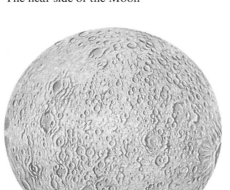

Figure 5b
The far side of the Moon.

Figure 6
Io, a moon of Jupiter.

Tides in space

Since the Moon produces tidal effects on the Earth, you might expect the Earth to produce tidal effects on the Moon. That is just what seems to have happened in the past. But the Moon is much smaller and has therefore always stored less energy. Tidal forces have slowed it down, so that it is now no longer spinning. So the Moon now keeps the same face towards the Earth. But tidal forces from the Sun still cause moonquakes.
Other moons in space are still going through this process. Tides have dramatic effects on Jupiter's moon Io. Jupiter is more than 300 times more massive than the Earth. Io is similar to our own Moon. There are no seas on Io and the tides distort the whole moon. The work done by huge forces moving is so great that it heats up the inside of Io and causes tremendous volcanic activity.

Section **E**3.3   **Exploring space**

The first record of human interest in space must be a bone from the Stone Age, at least 6000 years ago. It has phases of the Moon carved upon it, and was some sort of calendar.

Several ancient civilizations studied the Sun, Moon and stars. The Chinese kept very accurate records, particularly of unusual events such as the brief appearances of bright stars and those of visiting comets. The Arabs named many stars, and the Greeks grouped them into constellations. All used the objects in the sky for navigation and marking the passage of the seasons. Just as happens nowadays, some people would try to tell the future by looking at the stars.

Even today, scientists still explore space mainly by observing from the ground. For this they rely on electromagnetic radiation from space. Electromagnetic waves can travel through the vacuum of space and bring us information about the Universe.

1 What type of electromagnetic radiation have you used to observe the Universe? What other types of electromagnetic radiation are there?

Have you ever tried to count the stars? It is an impossible task. Thousands of years ago, the writer of the psalms said that only God knows them all. If you go out on a clear night, you can see so many stars even in a tiny area of

Figure 1
The Schmidt telescope in China.

the sky. The longer you watch, the more sensitive your eye becomes and the more you can see. If you then use a pair of binoculars, you find that there are even more stars in the area you looked at with your naked eye. Even today, scientists can only estimate how many there may be.

2 Choose a small patch of clear night sky and count how many stars you can see easily. Use this to estimate how many you can see altogether.

The problem with observing the night sky is that so many objects are dim. Astronomers use giant telescopes to gather light from the dimmest objects in the Universe. Our atmosphere does not help. Dirty air with light from cars and street lamps makes observing difficult. So astronomers place telescopes on high mountains, above the thickest part of the atmosphere. Even so, the moving air spoils the sharpness of the images.

Radio waves are another kind of electromagnetic radiation that astronomers can use to observe the Universe from the surface of the Earth. Large radio telescope dishes gather and focus the radio waves. You may have heard of Jodrell Bank, one of the earliest radio telescopes to use a large dish. Today there are many other radio telescopes. Some use a number of smaller receivers spaced over several miles. The largest radio telescopes use receivers in different parts of the World to act like a telescope of the same diameter as the Earth.

3 A satellite television disc is like a radio telescope. Draw a diagram of one and show how it gathers and reflects waves.

Figure 2
The Mark 1A radio telescope at Jodrell Bank.

Satellite telescopes

Signals come from the Universe in other forms of electromagnetic radiation, but most of these are partly shielded out by the atmosphere. Since 1957, when Sputnik, the first man-made satellite, was launched, astronomers have been able to send telescopes above the Earth's atmosphere. They have used remote-controlled infra-red, ultra-violet, X-ray and gamma-ray telescopes in satellites around the Earth. These show that some objects in the Universe emit tremendous amounts of invisible radiation, suggesting that powerful processes are happening within them.

Some satellite telescopes have been more successful than others. In 1990 astronomers used the space shuttle to put the Hubble Space Telescope into orbit above the atmosphere. This telescope was designed to give very clear pictures with visible light. The launch was fine but a major mistake was made by those who made and tested the mirror. So, unfortunately, the telescope itself is not of the best quality. There are plans for astronauts to repair it.

4 What sorts of mistakes that you make in your experiments are like those that real scientists could make?

Figure 3
The Hubble telescope in orbit.

Going there

Nevertheless, there really is no substitute for 'going there'. Scientists have explored most of the Solar System with automatic, unmanned spacecraft, called probes. Their voyages can be lengthy. Voyager 2 passed Jupiter, Saturn and Uranus, and finally reached Neptune after twelve years. Some probes have two parts, an **orbiter** which provides images of a planet from space, and a **lander** which gathers surface samples for analysis. The two Viking landers checked the soil on Mars for life but found none.

The most adaptable and intelligent 'machines' in space are humans. The first spaceman was Yuri Gagarin (a Russian) in 1961 and the first man to set foot on the Moon was Neil Armstrong (an American) in 1969. In all, twelve Americans, on six Apollo missions, landed on the Moon. They collected samples of moon rock and set up many scientific instruments, such as 'moonquake' detectors. In the later missions, they took an electric vehicle with them to travel around on the Moon. The Apollo Moon landings finished in December 1972. In a world where technology is advancing constantly, you may be surprised to know that they marked the peak of American manned space travel. Apart from building a reusable spacecraft (the shuttle), little has been done since.

Since the time of Apollo, Soviet scientists have concentrated on using space stations in Earth orbit. Some of their cosmonauts spent a year on board to investigate the effects of prolonged space travel on the human body. For political reasons, both the USA and Russia spend much less money on space exploration nowadays. Some scientists discuss the possibility of a manned trip to Mars. But a trip like that would take two years and would be so expensive that it would need co-operation between several nations working together.

5 Write an equipment list for a two-year manned trip to Mars.

Figure 4
A view of the Martian landscape from one of the Viking landers.

Figure 5
A view of Neptune from Voyager 2.

Figure 6
Collecting a lunar rock sample.

Figure 7
An artist's impression of a future space station.

Section E3.4   Space geology

Figure 1
A meteorite which landed in the Ukraine.

Have you ever seen a 'shooting star'? If you look into a clear night sky, particularly in the Autumn, there is a chance that you will see one. They are small star-like points of light that shoot across the sky in a few seconds. These **meteors** are small bodies that orbit around the Sun and enter into the Earth's atmosphere. Usually, friction between a body and the atmosphere causes it to get hot, glow and then melt. Very occasionally, the body is large enough to keep on going right through the atmosphere and hit the Earth's surface. Then scientists call it a **meteorite**. Until the Space Age, evidence from meteorites was the only source of information about geology in the rest of the Solar System. Scientists could only guess what the surfaces of other worlds looked like.

In Arizona, USA, a crater was formed by the impact of a huge meteorite. Scientists estimate that it probably had the mass of an oil tanker and hit the Earth about 50 000 years ago. Such a big meteorite is very rare. But many smaller lumps of rock wander into the Earth's path and crash onto the surface. Some are dense lumps of iron and nickel with marks of slow cooling, called Widmanstatten patterns. They may have come from the core of a planet destroyed in the early, violent history of our Solar System.

1 Find out, or estimate, the mass of a large oil tanker. How big would a meteorite of the same mass be?

Figure 2
Meteor Crater, Arizona.

Over the last thirty years scientists have learned much more about space geology. Space probes have visited seven of the planets, leaving only distant Pluto unexplored. The pictures sent back have revealed that our own planet is unique. It is the only planet with life, and the only one showing evidence of plate tectonics.

The inner planets

In order of distance from the Sun, there are four small solid planets: Mercury, Venus, Earth and Mars. These are called the **terrestrial planets**, because in some ways they are all rather like the Earth. These planets have dense cores, probably of iron, rock mantles and outer crusts.

Though all the inner planets show signs of geological activity in the past, only the Earth is still definitely active. The surface of Mercury is pock-marked with craters, caused by many collisions with material around the Solar System. Venus is nearly the twin of the Earth. It is covered with thick clouds of carbon dioxide which only let a dim orange glow through. So scientists have to use radar to investigate the surface of the planet. Volcano-shaped landforms are present, but the radar cannot show whether or not these are still active.

Mars seems to have had much volcanic activity in the past. There are several extinct volcanoes like those on Earth. Olympus Mons is the biggest. It is more than three times as high as Mount Everest and big enough to cover most of Britain. Olympus Mons is a basalt shield volcano, like some volcanoes in Hawaii. Its cone shape has gently sloping sides because of the very runny lava that the volcano produced.

Figure 3
Radar image of part of the surface of Venus.

Figure 4
A canyon on Mars. This one is 3000 km long and up to 8 km deep!

2 Explain why runny lava would make a shallow cone. Draw the shape of volcano you would expect if the lava were not runny.

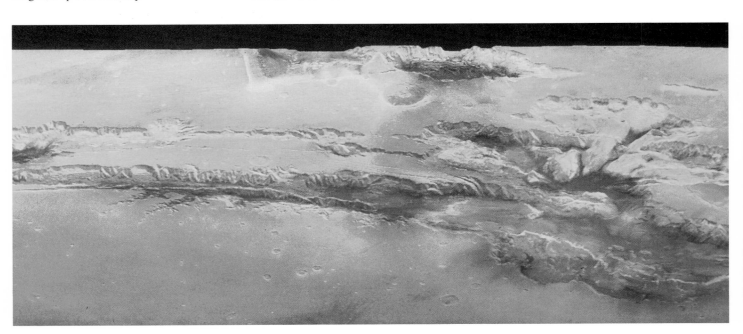

The outer planets

The outer planets are very different from the inner ones. Jupiter, Saturn, Uranus and Neptune are not solid bodies, but giant balls of gas. They are mostly hydrogen and helium with small amounts of other gases, particularly ammonia and methane. The outer planets have cores as well, but these are tiny and very dense.

3 What elements make up ammonia and methane? Write their chemical formulae.

Jupiter is the biggest planet. Its core probably consists of liquid hydrogen with a rocky centre. The surface temperature of Jupiter is very cold, about − 100 °C. But the core has a temperature of 20 000 °C and a pressure of 50 000 000 atmospheres. Under such enormous pressure hydrogen behaves like a metal and can conduct electricity. The other planets are probably similar. All of them have magnetic fields which seem to be made by electric currents in their cores.

4 Draw a loop of electric current and the magnetic field it would produce.

All the outer planets have moons, and most of these are composed of ice, like Saturn's moon Enceladus. Internal heating in the past has caused the surface to crack and shift in the same sort of way that we see happening on our own Earth when icebergs move on water.

Triton, the largest moon of Neptune, is unusual. It has its own greenhouse coating made from solidified gas. The Sun's rays pass through this layer and boil trapped, liquefied nitrogen and hydrocarbons under the surface. The puffs of gas produced make plumes of sooty 'smoke'. It is rather like having a volcano at very low temperatures.

You read about the most geologically active body in the Solar System on page 41. Jupiter's moon Io is heated by tidal forces. Io's surface is continuously changing as volcanoes produce dark sulphurous eruptions.

The Earth has oceans and rivers. These are only possible on a warm planet with an atmosphere. Venus and Mars were the only other possible candidates for possessing such conditions, since Mercury is airless and too hot, while the other planets are too cold. The carbon dioxide layer on Venus traps the Sun's rays like a greenhouse. It may once have had water vapour in the atmosphere, but this would have escaped into space a long time ago. Before space exploration, it was thought that Mars might have Earth-like conditions. Unfortunately, although pictures of the Martian surface show river valleys, there is no sign of running water today. If the planet did have water, it dried up long ago. Mars today is a very dry, frigid desert with only a thin atmosphere of carbon dioxide, quite unsuitable for life. Earth is the only place we can call home!

5 Make a list of the chemicals mentioned in this section. From it, work out what elements you know you could find on other planets.

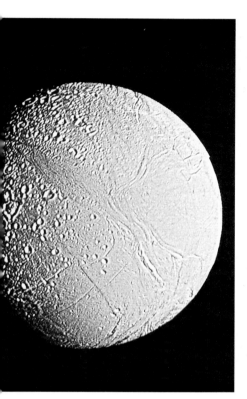

Figure 5
A view of Enceladus, a moon of Saturn, from Voyager 2.

Section E3.5 Air for life!

In the month of May, in Britain, you can usually hear the scream of swifts as they circle around high in the sky. They are only one of the common birds that visit us in summer. There are two other very common birds that are very similar, and also arrive in spring – the house martin and the swallow.

1 Find out how swifts, house martins and swallows differ, and what they all feed on.

If your house has overhanging eaves, you may have house martins nesting under them. They seem such friendly birds. The young poke their heads out of the nests, and the adults fly around collecting food, quite unworried by human observers a few feet below. But it is not just summer that martins need; they also need clean air. They do not live in polluted areas. Shakespeare wrote 'Where they breed and haunt, the air is delicate'.

If an observer from outer space looked at our Solar System he might say the same about humans. This is a reminder that the right sort of air is necessary for human life. Neither the carbon dioxide atmosphere of Venus and Mars, nor the cold hydrogen on the outer planets can keep life going. Humans can only live on Earth. Technology produces air pollution as well as good things. And since the atmosphere is essential for life, scientists need to understand it, so that they can advise us what to do to keep it pure enough to sustain life.

2 What chemicals which cause air pollution does technology produce?

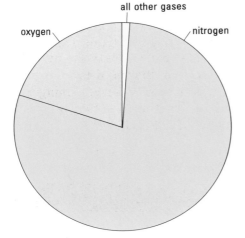

Figure 1
Gases in the air.

You can read in figure 1 about the gases that air contains. The most important ones of these for life are oxygen and carbon dioxide. Plants and animals alike need oxygen for **respiration**. Recently scientists have discovered that oxygen has another role as well. In the upper atmosphere, cosmic rays from the Sun constantly bombard the oxygen. This converts ordinary oxygen molecules (O_2) to **ozone** molecules (O_3) and produces an **ozone layer** in the upper atmosphere. It acts as a shield, protecting you from harmful ultra-violet radiation from the Sun.

Plants need the carbon dioxide in the atmosphere for **photosynthesis**. In this process, plants take in carbon dioxide, join it up with water to make chemicals like glucose, and give out oxygen.

Once, living organisms alone kept the balance between photosynthesis and respiration. This balance kept steady the levels of oxygen and carbon dioxide. Green plants produced oxygen from carbon dioxide. All living organisms then used this oxygen and produced carbon dioxide, which was again used by the plants. Large forest fires could shift this balance, using much oxygen and producing much carbon dioxide. But nowadays there is evidence that man shifts the balance himself by burning fossil fuels.

3 Write a chemical equation for the burning of a fossil fuel.

The greenhouse effect

Carbon dioxide in the atmosphere acts rather like a greenhouse does. It helps trap the Sun's radiation. If there is more carbon dioxide in the atmosphere, the planet gets hotter. On page 46 you read about the greenhouse effect on Venus, which makes it so hot. Many people are worried about the greenhouse effect occurring on the Earth.

Over the last hundred years, the amount of carbon dioxide in the atmosphere has increased. This has happened at the same time as man has been burning a lot of fossil fuels. Environmental scientists are trying to find out whether these two facts are connected. To do this they need to understand those natural processes which affect the atmosphere. If things in the past happened in the same way as they do today, then the study of Geology can help, because rocks contain evidence of the chemical composition of the atmosphere in the past.

Forming the atmosphere

Figure 2
Stromatolites in Western Australia.

You read on page 30 that there is evidence that the Earth is 4600 million years old. If so, it probably started off with no atmosphere. Like the surfaces of other planets, it would have been bombarded by rock and iron meteorites and icy comets. The iron would have sunk to the core, releasing energy and, together with energy released from radioactivity, this would have made the Earth very hot. This in turn would have produced volcanic activity over the entire surface of the Earth, releasing carbon dioxide just like volcanoes today. So the Earth's first atmosphere was probably carbon dioxide.

In rocks dated 3500 million years old, scientists have found the first fossils of bacteria-like organisms. In slightly younger rocks there are calcium carbonate deposits from sorts of bacteria called **stromatolites**. Photosynthesis by stromatolites would have reduced the carbon dioxide level in the atmosphere and increased the oxygen level. Their activity would also have made a thin ozone layer.

There are banded ironstones left by long-disappeared seas. These are iron (III) oxides dated about 2200 million years ago. They give evidence that the oxygen level was then high enough to oxidize iron(II) ions in seawater to iron(III) ions.

Figure 3
A sample of banded ironstone.

4 Write a chemical equation, involving an iron(II) compound, and an iron(III) compound.

Perhaps 400 million years ago, the ozone layer became thick enough to protect organisms out of water. Then photosynthesizing plants could invade the land and produce even more oxygen. 100 million years later the carboniferous coal forests grew near the Equator and the oxygen levels probably peaked before sinking slightly to present levels.

In the meantime, volcanoes would have continued to produce carbon dioxide, which was largely used up, and nitrogen, which would simply build up to present levels. Even then, carbon dioxide levels evidently fluctuated and its greenhouse properties probably affected the world's climate.

You can see how important the ozone layer is in this story. That is why scientists worry about the gases called CFCs (chlorofluorocarbons). CFCs used to be used in aerosols and are still used in refrigerators. There is evidence that, in a few decades, they have destroyed some of the ozone layer that took many years to form.

Figure 4
An artist's impression of the dawn of life.

Figure 5
Weather balloons being launched to investigate the hole in the ozone layer over the Arctic.

Figure 6
The ozone layer protects you while you're sunbathing.

5 The ozone layer protects you against ultra-violet light. What is ultra-violet light? What harmful effects does it have?

Section E3.6 Stars, old and young

It is easy to see that some stars are brighter than others. If you look at stars carefully, especially with binoculars, you will see that they have different colours as well. With a good astronomical telescope, these differences are even more visible. They encouraged astrophysicists to try to study the physics of stars at a distance. When astrophysicists try to understand what happens in the rest of the universe, they assume that things a long way away behave in just the same way that they do here. This is another example of the principle of uniformity that you read about on page 27.

1 What happens to the colour of a glowing piece of metal when you increase the temperature? What information might you be able to deduce from the colour of a star?

Last century, astronomers started cataloguing the different kinds of stars. They assumed that the colour of a star gives information about its temperature. Hotter stars are blue in colour, medium temperature ones are yellow, and cooler stars are orange-red. You may think that this is a sensible guess, because a red hot object becomes more yellow when it gets hotter. Astronomers have more evidence about the temperature than that. They use a device called a **spectroscope** to examine the spectrum of light from a star.

2 Draw a diagram to show how you would use a prism to investigate a star's spectrum.

You may have used a prism to make a spectrum from a white light source. This spreads the colours apart, from red to violet. But if you pass white light through a hot gas before making a spectrum, you find that the gas absorbs some of the light. This leaves the spectrum with blank parts called **absorption lines** (figure 1). Light escaping from the centre of any star passes through the

Figure 1
The absorption line spectrum of the Sun.

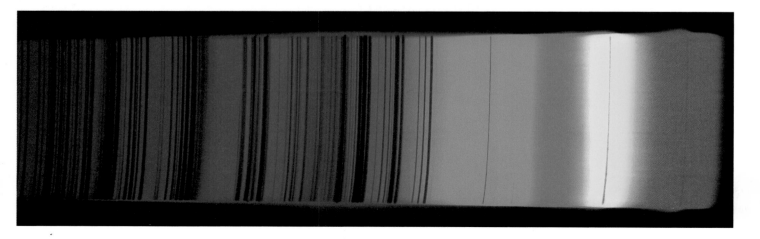

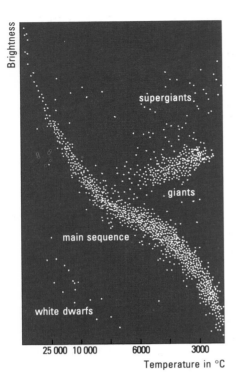

Figure 2
The Hertzsprung-Russell diagram shows how the brightness of a star is related to its temperature.

gases at its surface. From the absorption lines, astronomers can tell both the types of gas present and the temperature of the gas. They can recognize that blue stars are hot because they have few lines, and that red stars are cool because they have many groups of lines.

> **3** From the Earth, astronomers used absorption lines to detect the carbon dioxide atmospheres of Mars and Venus. What light source did they use? How did they do it?

You know that a weak torch close to your eye can seem brighter than car headlights which are a long way away. In the same way, stars which are shining brightly a long way from the Earth may seem dimmer than fainter stars which are closer. The stars Sirius and Rigel are visible on winter nights. Rigel gives out 350 times more light than Sirius but looks fainter because it is 100 times further away.

Fortunately, astronomers have a number of different ways of measuring how far stars are from us. From the distance, and from how bright the star seems from Earth, they can work out how much light it is actually giving out. Early this century, two scientists, Hertzsprung and Russell, used this information to work out a pattern that connects the spectrum of a star with how much light it gives out. They devised a graph, called an Hertzsprung-Russell diagram (figure 2). Nearly all the stars fit in a central band called the **main sequence**. Thus, hot blue stars are big and give out a lot of light. Cool red dwarf stars are small and faint. Our Sun is near the middle.

The life of a star

Stars start as clouds of gas and dust. In line with what you read about gravitation on page 37, all parts of the cloud pull each other together with a

Figure 3
The Orion Nebula.

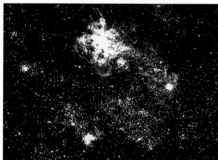

Figure 4
Before and after views of a supernova,
which appears as the bright spot to the
right of the lower picture.

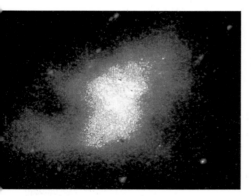

Figure 5
The Crab Nebula.

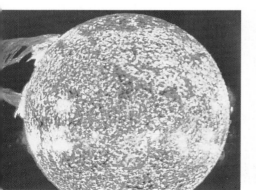

Figure 6
Turbulence on the surface of the Sun.

gravitational force. There is so much matter in a star that the forces cause enormous pressures. A tremendous amount of work is done as the star pulls itself together and this causes the temperature to rise. This is the explanation for the conditions you read about in the centre of the planet Jupiter on page 47. When the centre of the cloud reaches 10 million degrees Celsius the nuclear fusion of hydrogen to helium begins and the star begins to shine. Its life span depends on how much matter is there, its temperature and how much light it gives out.

A blue star can be 80 000 times brighter than our Sun but there is only enough fuel for three million years. Finally it is expected to explode as a **supernova**, giving out very bright light that outshines the whole galaxy for a short time. Then it leaves nothing but debris and a collapsed core. Gravity pulls the core together and squashes electrons in the atoms into the nucleus. They join with protons to make a **neutron star**, where a piece the size of a pinhead would have a mass of millions of tons. If there is enough matter, the gravitational forces cause further collapse and the matter disappears to the nothingness of a **black hole**.

The life expectancy of our Sun is about 10 000 million years. When it runs out of hydrogen fuel it is expected to swell to become a red giant star and swallow up the Earth. The outer gaseous layer of the red giant may then gently blow out into space and form a **planetary nebula**. A tiny hot core will be left at the centre of, possibly, a very dense white dwarf star.

4 A proton and an electron can join to make a neutron. Explain how four hydrogen atoms could make a helium atom.

5 What is an estimated age of the Earth? If the Sun is the same age, how much life does it have left?

Our Sun is alone, but many other stars have partners. If one of them is very dense, either a white dwarf, a neutron star or a black hole, its gravitational field can be strong enough to attract bursts of gas from the other of the pair. This can cause repeated explosions with bursts of light given off. A star giving out light like this is called a **nova**.

Figure 7
The Helix Nebula, a planetary nebula.

Section **E**3.7 **How did it all begin?**

Whatever we believe, it is difficult to look at the night sky without a sense of how marvellous it is. The more we observe it, the more wonderful it appears. Perhaps the stars remind us how small we are and how big the Universe is. They may simply overwhelm us with their beauty. In any case, few of us can spend a few minutes looking without being moved by the experience.

The philosopher Immanuel Kant (1724–1804) said 'Two things fill the mind with ever-increasing wonder and awe, the more often and the more intensely the mind of thought is drawn to them: the starry heavens above me and the moral law within me.' From quite a different perspective, the writer of the psalms said 'When I consider your heavens, the work of your fingers, the Moon and the stars, which you have set in place, what is man that you care for him?'

Being so wonderful, the Universe seems always to have caused man to wonder how it all began. As scientific knowledge has progressed, scientists have been more able to develop theories of how the Universe was formed. This helps us to think about how the Universe is changing and how it might end. But questions like 'Who made it?' and 'Why was it made?' are not ones that science can ever answer.

If we want to understand just how big the Universe might be, let's start with something small! The Big Bang theory suggests that the whole Universe started off about a tenth of a millimetre across. That is smaller than the full stop at the end of this sentence.

Ten thousand times larger than this are the children in this picture. They are one metre tall.

A thousand times larger again is the City of London. It is about 1 kilometre across.

1 Which questions about the Universe has your study of science answered? Which has it not answered?

Our own interest in the Universe tells us much about ourselves. We know about vast timescales and the huge extent of space. Our telescopes reveal countless galaxies, each with billions of stars, many of which may have planets like our own. It seems that we live on an insignificant planet, orbiting an average star, near the edge of a typical spiral galaxy, somewhere in a huge and very old Universe. And yet we desire and expect to understand not only the Universe but also our own place in the order of things.

2 What are the things about mankind that you think make us special?

Questions about the Universe are being investigated in two very different ways. While astronomers look deep into the vastness of space, nuclear physicists are investigating the behaviour of tiny particles, smaller than the atom, that make the Universe function and which played a part in its creation.

You may have noticed that a police or ambulance siren has a lower pitch when the vehicle drives away from you. Early this century, astronomers made a similar observation about the light from stars. They noticed that most of the light was redder than they expected. This **redshift** suggests that stars are moving away from the Earth as the Universe is expanding. Edwin Hubble (1889–1953) developed a theory which states that the furthest objects are moving fastest from us and have the greatest redshift.

3 What happens to the sound from a siren when a vehicle drives towards you? What do you think light from a star that is moving towards us looks like?

Astronomers use large telescopes, fitted with sensitive electronic detectors, to observe very dim objects and measure their redshifts. From this they can estimate how far they are from us. The distances are so huge that they are measured in light years. A light year is the distance travelled by light in one year. That is 9.5 million million kilometres.

4 A rocket which launches a satellite can travel at about 9.5 kilometres per second. How long would it take to travel a light year?

We can observe galaxies with very bright centres, called **quasars**, at distances up to 15 000 million light years. It is astonishing to realize that the light from these bodies took 15 000 million years to reach us. We are seeing quasars not as they are, but as they were, long before the Earth was formed. This is like looking back through time towards the beginning of the Universe.

Great Britain is about 1000 kilometres long, a thousand times larger again. 1000 kilometres is 1 megametre (1 Mm).

If we could see even further, would we find the edge of the Universe? There seem to be two reasons why not. First, space is curved in a way that means no matter how far we look, we just see more of it. Looking at the horizon on Earth is similar. The horizon appears to be the edge, but if we travel towards it we see more beyond. The second problem is that the Universe is like an expanding bubble and the galaxies in the most distant parts are moving away from us at nearly the speed of light. No light from them can ever reach us, so we cannot see them. This visual limit probably does not mark the edge of the Universe; theories predict much more exists beyond, which is forever unseen to us.

Big bang or steady state?

Hubble's work resulted in the **big bang** theory. This suggested that the Universe began between 10 and 20 thousand million years ago as a hot, exploding bubble of space containing matter, energy, forces and time that make up the Universe today.

In 1948 Fred Hoyle, Hermann Bondi and Thomas Gold put forward a different theory. They suggested that the Universe is gently expanding and that new matter is continuously being created in the gaps between existing matter. In this theory, the Universe has no beginning or end; it had always been in existence. This is called the **steady state** theory.

So forty years ago there were two very different theories on the beginning of the Universe. It has taken some time for scientists to choose one of them.

5 Is it surprising that scientists should suggest two quite different theories? What scientific theories do you expect will change in your lifetime?

1000 Mm is more than twice the distance from the Earth to the Moon. This is a thousand times larger than Great Britain.

1 000 000 Mm would include the orbits of the Earth, Mars and Jupiter around the Sun.

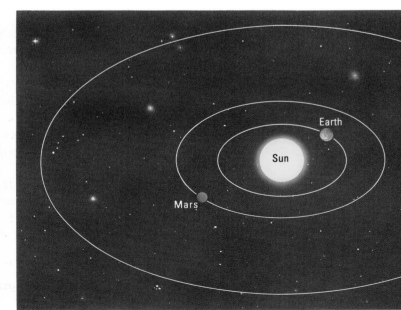

By examining the evidence, astrophysicists have come to accept the big bang model as the best theory (for the moment!). They have found that distant objects, such as quasars, are unlike nearby galaxies. This means that the Universe was different in the past. The steady state theory would predict that things in the past would have been the same. Astronomers also measured the average temperature of space by examining the microwave radiation it gives out. This temperature is 2.7 kelvin ($-270.45\,°C$), higher than the steady state theory would predict.

6 You know that scientists use the principle of uniformity to develop their theories. Explain which theory, steady state or big bang, is closer to this principle.

1000 million Mm is about one-tenth of a light year, and would include a huge amount of space around our Solar system, but we are still only one-fortieth of the way to the next nearest star.

1 million million Mm – about 100 light years – would include some but not all of our galaxy.

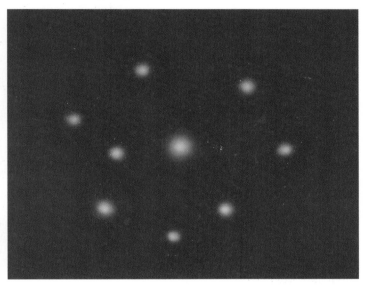

The first day

When scientists extend the big bang theory a long way backwards, it is eventually difficult to make it fit with the principle of uniformity. But it is fun to use the theory to guess at what the beginnings of the Universe might have been like. Some of the numbers must be expressed in standard form, since they are either are too large or too small to write in any other understandable way.

The theory predicts that in the first fractions of a second (10^{-43} s), the whole Universe was probably only a tenth of millimetre across. It was unbelievably hot ($10^{35}\,°C$) and all the forces, electromagnetic, gravitational and nuclear, behaved the same way. Time did not really exist and there may have been at least ten dimensions!

A further fraction of a second (10^{-35} s) later, the force of gravity had departed from the others and the temperature had fallen to $10^{28}\,°C$. The ten or more dimensions collapsed into three plus the fourth, time. At this point

1000 million million Mm – about 100 000 light years – would include the whole of our galaxy, the Milky Way.

1 million million million Mm – about 1 million light years – would include clusters of many whole galaxies.

the Universe entered the **inflation epoch** and expanded from a centimetre to hundreds of billions of light years across in a minute instant of time. Afterwards the Universe continued to expand but more slowly.

7 Write out the times and temperatures in the above two paragraphs without using standard form.

The early Universe contained radiation and matter, which were constantly changing into each other. Electromagnetic radiation produced both matter and anti-matter. Matter and anti-matter combined again to produce more radiation: particles and anti-particles annihilated each other in staggering numbers, leaving only radiation. As the Universe expanded, the temperature fell and the process operated in one direction only. Our Universe exists, so the amount of matter must have outnumbered the amount of anti-matter by one millionth of a percent. The tiny difference went on to form all the atoms in the Universe today.

By the end of the first thousandth of a second, a whole range of strange heavy particles, each smaller than an atom, had disappeared. A minute later, the remaining neutrons and protons began to fuse together, into hydrogen (mainly) and helium nuclei. The Universe literally detonated like a fusion bomb.

8 Imagine being there to watch the first day of the creation of the Universe. Write about what you would think and feel.

From atoms to galaxies

Much later, around 300 000 years from the start, the temperature had fallen to 4000 °C. The hydrogen nuclei and electrons then combined into atoms. From then onwards there were no free electrons to scatter the light. A foggy Universe had become clear. This dramatic stage is called the **decoupling era**.

Perhaps 1000 million years later, the matter was still mainly hydrogen. Gravity began to pull the matter together and form stars, galaxies and clusters of galaxies. Our Universe is 'lumpy'. It seems that matter gathered in **cosmic strings** where there were streams of energy left over from the early Universe. An estimated 10 000 million years further on, our Sun and Solar System begin to form from gas and dust.

9 A proton and an electron can fuse to make a neutron. Explain how many protons and electrons are needed to make an iron atom.

The big bang theory itself still does not tell us what will eventually happen. As you read on page 38, gravitational forces still pull our Universe together and slow down the rate of expansion. So there are two possible outcomes. The first is that the Universe will keep expanding for ever, becoming thinner and thinner in the process. The other is that gravitational forces will halt the expansion, then the Universe will collapse. That suggests that the process might then begin all over again with another big bang!

Once again scientists are trying to decide between two possibilities. It all depends on how much matter there is in the Universe. Of course, even on the longest predictions, our Sun will have exploded and our Earth be dead, so mankind will not be affected. But you can be sure that it does not stop scientists wondering!

1000 million million million Mm would include the whole of the observable Universe.

Index